YESTER

My Life With the Beatles

Alistair Taylor

with Hal Schuster and Martin Roberts

A rare photo of the author, far right, with the Beatles.
(Courtesy Keystone Collection)

OTHER PIONEER BOOKS

•FISTS OF FURY: THE FILMS OF BRUCE LEE
Written by Edward Gross. March, 1990. $14.95, ISBN #1-55698-233-X
•WHO WAS THAT MASKED MAN?
Written by James Van Hise. March, 1990. $14.95, ISBN #1-55698-227-5
•PAUL MCCARTNEY: 20 YEARS ON HIS OWN
Written by Edward Gross. February, 1990. $9.95, ISBN #1-55698-263-1
•THE DARK SHADOWS TRIBUTE BOOK
Written by Edward Gross and James Van Hise. February, 1990. $14.95, ISBN#1-55698-234-8
•THE UNOFFICIAL TALE OF BEAUTY AND THE BEAST, 2nd Edition
Written by Edward Gross. $14.95, 164 pages, ISBN #1-55698-261-5
•TREK: THE LOST YEARS
Written by Edward Gross. $12.95, 128 pages, ISBN #1-55698-220-8
•THE TREK ENCYCLOPEDIA
Written by John Peel. $19.95, 368 pages, ISBN#1-55698-205-4
•HOW TO DRAW ART FOR COMIC BOOKS
Written by James Van Hise. $14.95, 160 pages, ISBN#1-55698-254-2
•THE TREK CREW BOOK
Written by James Van Hise. $9.95, 112 pages, ISBN#1-55698-256-9
•THE MAKING OF THE NEXT GENERATION
Written by Edward Gross. $14.95, 128 pages, ISBN#1-55698-219-4
•BATMANIA
Written by James Van Hise. $14.95, 176 pages, ISBN#1-55698-252-6
•GUNSMOKE
Written by John Peel. $14.95, 204 pages, ISBN#1-55698-221-6
•ELVIS-THE MOVIES: THE MAGIC LIVES ON
Written by Hal Schuster. $14.95, ISBN#1-55698-223-2
•STILL ODD AFTER ALL THESE YEARS: ODD COUPLE COMPANION.
Written by Edward Gross. $12.95, 132 pages, ISBN#1-55698-224-0
•SECRET FILE: THE UNOFFICIAL MAKING OF A WISEGUY
Written by Edward Gross. $14.95, 164 pages, ISBN#1-55698-261-5
•NEW KIDS ON THE BLOCK
Written by Scott Nance. $9.95, 100 pages
•ZZ TOP: RECYCLING THE BLUES
Written by Scott Nance. $9.95, 100 pages
•FAB FILMS OF THE BEATLES
Written by Edward Gross. $14.95, 164 pages, ISBN#1-55698-244-5

Designed and Edited by Hal Schuster

Library of Congress Cataloging-in-Publication Data
Alistair Taylor

1.. YESTERDAY: My Life With the Beatles (biography)
I. Title

Based on an edition first published in Great Britain in 1988 by Sidgwick & Jackson Limited

Published by Pioneer Books, Inc., 5715 N. Balsam Rd., Las Vegas, NV, 89130.

Revised edition first Printing, 1991

To all the Beatle fans who asked me to write this book

ACKNOWLEDGEMENTS

My thanks to Bart Andrews, who was the first to take me on board; to my e England, Susan Hill, she was so helpful and constructive. To Martin, Win, Judy for their help and patience through the birth pains! A special thank you to Mark Lapidos, a dear friend and without whom....and a very, very special thank you to my patient and long suffering wife, Lesley, who has put up with my personal Beatlemania for all these years.

The author searching for the magic island,
Greece, 1968.
(Alistair Taylor)

1
CHAPTER

Liverpool

Yesterday I sold my last piece of wood in the timber yard! Yes, I've found a new job, starting to-day. I was really fed up working at William Evans. They were a friendly enough crowd of people to work with, but the job itself just didn't suit me at all. Who wants to sell wood for the rest of his life?

So I started to look through the Sits Vac column in the Liverpool Echo. I didn't really have anything particular in mind, as long as it was interesting, legal and paid a million pounds a year! Some days went by before anything eye-catching appeared, then a few days ago I spotted an advertisement saying: "Young man wanted for position as Sales Assistant in city centre record store..." This was more like it. You know how much I love music; I even spent my first wage-packet on records. There can't be a jazz club in Liverpool that I haven't been in. I love selling things, too, and the thought of actually being paid to sell records was really tempting. Lesley liked the idea too. Being the wife of a dissatisfied woodman with a secret lust for show business can't have been easy.

Straightaway I wrote off for an interview to Mr Brian Epstein, of NEMS Limited, Whitechapel, Liverpool, and waited in keen anticipation to see what would happen. North End Music Stores, to give NEMS its full title, is quite a big local business and it seemed like a very useful job to have. A few days later the reply came: would I go for an interview with Mr Brian Epstein? Would I!

I turned up not just on time, but early, and spent a while looking at the NEMS shop. It looked very efficiently run and I couldn't wait to get behind the counter among all those records. There were even shelves of record catalogues and reference books bigger than telephone directories. Heaven!

At last I was asked to go up to Mr. Epstein's office on the first floor. Mr Epstein is a young man, the son of Mr Harold Epstein, the owner of the firm. He's very much the up-and-coming businessman, in an immaculately pressed suit and white shirt. Everything he says is very definite and precise and I felt that he was really giving me a good inspection.

We talked for a very long time about all sorts of things, especially my career, which has been fairly checkered! He thawed out a lot when he discovered that I love jazz and know a bit about it. He's really an enthusiast of classical music and I think he knows another music fan when he sees one, even if our tastes are different.

I mustn't put him in a pigeonhole, though. I've asked around a bit and it seems that he's got quite a reputation as the best record retailer in Liverpool, with an ability to tell which records are going to be hits — very useful!

The interview seemed to be going well, but nothing definite had been said about whether I was going to be offered the job. At last Mr Epstein leaned back, carefully inspected the backs of his fingers, and said, "Well, you can have a job as a Sales Assistant, but it doesn't pay very much. On the other hand, I've been thinking about hiring a Personal Assistant to help me with the general running of the business. Would you consider being my Personal Assistant and helping out on the counter selling records whenever it's necessary?"

You can imagine my reply! Then and there he gave me a job to do, even though I was still officially working for the timber yard. He had some bullfighting posters which he wanted to be framed. Would I see to it, please?

Of course, said I, thinking that he didn't seem to be quite the type to be interested in bullfighting. So off I went with the posters, gave in my notice to the timber yard and went home as Personal Assistant to Mr Brian Epstein, record retailer.

Today I started working for NEMS full time. It's really a treasure-house for a record nut like me. Mr Epstein has a very simple stock-control system which keeps track of every record sold every day. This means that if we sell out of a record, or it isn't in stock, we know at once and we can order straight away; the only delay is the delivery time. This gives us the edge over every other store in town, and probably the country.

(Listen to me saying "we" and I've only been there for a day; it's just that exciting!)

One of the other people in the hop told me that top record retailers from London come up here to try to find out how he does it — but without success.

I spent today selling records, filling in order forms, doing all sorts of tasks for Mr Epstein and I wasn't bored once! The best fun so far is trying to get hold of rare records. The boast is that NEMS can supply a copy of any record that's still available. Oh yes, thought I, until I looked in the reference library of catalogues and trade publications. That's no boast, that's the truth. Now I know who's a big seller in Germany or France! Apparently this sort of detective work is going to be a big part of my job.

Mr Epstein was still wearing his immaculate business clothes in all this rush and activity. He doesn't seem to sweat or get scruffy during the day like the rest of us. At six o'clock he still looked freshly-pressed and fit to work on through the night. I think he's going to be a demanding employer, but an interesting one. It'll certainly take some time for me to find out what sort of a character he is, but I think it's going to be fun.

Now for bed. It's been a long day, but I think I've found a job which I'm going to like - selling plastic instead of wood!

Liverpool

I think "Georgia on my Mind" by Ray Charles is the most fantastic record to hit the charts this year and it's truly amazing to have a jazz artiste at Number One in the States. I hope you like it as much as I do.

Actually, there's a tale against myself connected with this record, so every time you play it you can think of me and reflect on what a jerk I am. Brian Epstein has a tremendous reputation for sniffing out hits in advance; well, every week I help Brian (you can tell we're on first name terms now!) to go through the new releases in the little office in Whitechapel and work out which are most likely to sell and how many we should stock of each.

Along came "Georgia on my Mind" and Brian at once said, "Alistair, that is going to be a Number One, without doubt!"

I just burst out laughing. "Brian, I adore it," I replied, "but it just isn't commercial. Jazz artistes don't get into the pop charts. A truly great disc, but not a hit in a million years!"

"Right, Alistair, we'll see which of us is right. I'll bet you a large gin and tonic that it will fly to Number One."

"You'll be buying, Brian. You're on."

I thought I was on to an easy winner. Brian doesn't particularly like pop music and although I don't go much for pop music myself I do know a bit about jazz. How could he tell that a jazz disc would do well in the pop charts?

But it has, of course. It cost me a large gin and tonic and taught me to respect Brian's extraordinary "nose" for a hit. He's promised to remind me if ever I cast doubts on his judgment again! So you play "Georgia on my Mind" for me and remind me every so often that I don't know as much as I think I do!

Liverpool

It seems like ages since I last wrote, but it's really only a few weeks. It's certainly been hectic for me and NEMS. There are great piles of records, almost to the ceiling — we've been stockpiling for the great British Christmas spending spree! We believe in doing things early here!

Brian writes a column called "Stop the World" in that magazine *Mersey Beat*, which covers the beat music scene in Liverpool. He reviews the latest pop releases and he certainly has his own opinions! This is one of the papers highly rated by the fans. There are all sorts of articles by musicians and disc-jockeys, as well as advertising by go-ahead record shops like NEMS.

I suppose that's it, really. He's a very shrewd operator, is Brian, and he likes the shop to come across as the best place for the beat fans to buy their discs. This means that we have to know everything about all the new releases and be able to lay our hands on any disc, wherever it's pressed.

For all that, Brian doesn't really seem to care for pop music. He's much more involved with classical music and anything with more of a rhythm that Beethoven isn't really his cup of tea. But business is his biggest concern and he wants us to sell as many as possible of every sort of record — pop, jazz, country and western, and classical.

My horizons have expanded a bit since I started tracking down rare records for our fanatical customers. I've always been a jazz man, with the occasional symphony thrown in as ballast, but now I have to say that some of these new groups can produce a good sound. I can't see myself going to one of the beat clubs, though. These are the places where the young groups are coming through, but the audiences are far too young for me, let alone Brian, to fit in with comfortably.

So it's all going along very well. From time to time, Brian makes me work until eight or nine at night, but he always takes me to dinner afterwards, to the 23 Club or to a city centre restaurant. There's also a super place called the Basnett Bar, which has a long old-fashioned marble counter and sells cockles by the plate. A plate of cockles and a glass of stout go down very well at times!

Brian's a strange employer. He's very demanding and he doesn't allow any inefficiency, but he's also very generous and friendly. He can get me into a rage and then minutes later have me laughing as if nothing's happened. Being a Personal Assistant needs a bit of tact and diplomacy on my part, but I'm learning bit by bit. Also, I have to be ready to go off and deal with any problems at a moment's notice. Still, I'm very happy in this job and it's streets better than clerking at the timber yard — and who knows where it might lead?

I'm now walking with a spring in my step!

Liverpool

A little incident happened in NEMS a few weeks ago. It's the only time I've ever watched that serial on television about the women's magazine— at Brian's request!

What's Alistair doing watching television programmes about women's magazines, just because his boss tells him to? Well, they showed an office party and they had John Leyton and his group on as the entertainment. Top Rank records really pushed their record, "Johnny Remember Me', as John Leyton's one of their young hopefuls. When their rep came around to NEMS, though, he didn't have a copy of the record to play to us, so we hadn't a clue about what it was like. It seemed a good idea to watch the programme on the evening the episode was on, so that we could judge the record and work out how many we were likely to sell. Oh, we're a proper *Juke Box Jury* here, but with one exception — Brian's hardly ever wrong about a record's hit potential.

When the evening came, Brian had a dinner date, so he asked me to watch the show and suggest how many copies we should stock in each of our shops. I quite liked the programme in a fairly mild way, but the record itself did nothing to me at all, so that was the message to Brian. We should stock no more than five copies in each shop, no more than the routine for a disc by an artist with no particular track record. Fine, said Brian, I'll be guided by you, Alistair, and we duly ordered that number.

The day after we put the order in to Top Rank records, back came their rep with a copy of the disc for us to hear. I remained totally underwhelmed by it (still am), but Brian's expression took on a thoughtful cast and he listened to it again.

"We'll take two hundred and fifty copies, please," he said.

Just like that, an awful lot to bet on one new record, but Brian was totally confident that "Johnny Remember Me" was going to be a big hit. I still wasn't so certain, but the day it was released we had a tremendous rush on it and it went very rapidly into the charts. The beauty of Brian's judgement was that for quite a while we were the only record shops on Merseyside that had any stocks of it!

That's the sort of business sense that I can only admire. When the kids came in to buy "Johnny Remember Me" they often as not went out with other records as well, so it boosted our profits all round. It seems the major labels pay great attention to Brian's orders, because they know the man can smell a hit a month away. I wish I had the gift, but it's pretty clear that I don't!

Liverpool

We've had a request for a record at NEMS and we can't find it in Brian's mighty filing system! I was behind the counter at Whitechapel this morning when in walked an ordinary-looking chap who introduced himself as Raymond Jones and asked me whether I could get hold of an unusual record for him. Well, that's my job and I've got shelves full of catalogues and directories to help me. No sweat, thought I.

"What's the title of the record and who's it by, then?" I asked him.

"It's called "My Bonnie" and it's by the Beatles."

"Let's see, then. Bee,double ee..."

"No. Beatles, spelt B-E-A-T-L-E-S."

"That's an odd way to spell it. Oh, I see, BEAT-les."

We don't have the record in stock, which didn't surprise me at all. I think I know every title we carry and that group's name is totally new to me. The odd thing is that I've looked in every reference book that Brian's got and I can't find a listing for the Beatles in any of them. I've spent hours going through all the old catalogues, to see if it has been deleted, but still no joy.

I don't like admitting failure to Brian, but this time I had to ask him for some help. The Beatles don't ring a bell with him either and even he can't find anything in the files. Well, if it exists, we can get it for Raymond Jones, but he'll have to give us some more information.

Liverpool

I feel a very dull dog, working away behind the counter at NEMS, while everyone's sunning themself on some distant beach!

In the end, Brian and I had to give up the search for "My Bonnie" as a bad job and wait until Raymond Jones came back into the shop, hoping to pick up his record. Sure enough, he appeared about a week later, expecting us to produce it like the magician's rabbit.

"We're having a bit of trouble finding this record, I'm afraid. Can you give us some more information about the Beatles, please? For instance, where do they play?" I asked him.

"Well, they've been in Germany recently, in Hamburg, I think. Oh yes, and they recorded something as the backing group for someone else. Is that any good?"

Not much, I thought, but I asked Raymond to call in a week and we would have something for him. The mention of Hamburg started me thinking that the band could have had the record released only in Germany, so I looked at the continental catalogues, which we hadn't paid much attention to first time around. A couple of minutes" search brought up what must be it: "My Bonnie" by Tony Sheridan and the Beat Brothers. That sounded near enough, although heaven knows where the name Beatles had come in.

The next step was to phone Polydor Records in Germany and ask for a copy of the record. There was the usual problem, a real drag for everyone at NEMS. Whenever we want to import a single copy of a record, we're forced by the record companies to buy a whole sealed box of twenty-five! This means that we make a whacking great loss on all our special import requests, unless we can unload these obscure records on to the unsuspecting public. Usually they moulder unsold in the storeroom until we clear them out. Brian doesn't mind the loss; it's our reputation for being able to supply any record that he's worried about. Compare these boxes of twenty-five to the two or three copies we order of each new British single we fancy or the hundreds of copies we might sell of Elvis, Cliff or Everleys records.

The odd thing was that while we were waiting for the box to arrive from Germany, several other people asked for the Beatles" record. Are we missing something? we thought. With Polydor's usual efficiency, the box arrived within a week and Raymond Jones and the other people collected their copies. It's not a bad record, but a bit basic, one of the new "beat" records which are all the rage in Liverpool. To get rid of the remaining twenty or so, Brian put up a little Sellotaped sign in the window: "Beatles Records For Sale Here', and put a copy in the "New Releases" bin.

It's absolutely amazing. Within a few hours, all the box had been sold and a week later the next two boxes we hastily ordered were sold out too. Who are these people? Brian got on the phone to Polydor's London distributors and told them how well their import was doing and suggested that they put it on general release in this country, but they wouldn't. We think they're missing a great opportunity, but it's a risky business and I suppose they know best. Still, you should see the kids asking for it. Who knows, if we create enough demand, they might have to release it. Oh dear, there I go, talking like a big businessman again, when I'm only a humble Personal Assistant!

Liverpool

We just found out The Beatles are a local group! All the time that Brian and I have been looking them up in the catalogues and supposing they were a German group, they were just a few short streets away, playing in the local beat clubs! No wonder their record sold out so quickly.

Brian was, to say the least, surprised that we didn't know such elementary facts about the music scene in our own back yard, so he asked me to find out a bit about the Beatles. It seems that they've been playing in Hamburg for quite a while, but they all come from Liverpool and are back in town. There are four of them: John Lennon, Paul McCartney, George Harrison and Pete Best and they use lead, rhythm and bass guitar and drums — the standard beat group line-up.

Brian's really been taking an interest in this group and he's asked me to find out which clubs they're playing at the moment. It turns out that they do lunchtime sessions at the Cavern Club in Mathew Street, only ten minutes" walk from our offices in Whitechapel. Brian has never been to the Cavern, but I remember it well from the days when it staged evening jazz sessions. It's really one of my old haunts — ah, memories of a misspent youth!

Now what's Brian aiming at, I wonder? He doesn't do anything in the music business without a very good reason, so he has some plan afoot. It's really very strange for him to take any interest at all in live pop music of any kind; I doubt if he's been to a pop concert in his life, for all his ability to spot the records that the kids will buy. So why the interest now in an unknown group, just because we shifted some of their records to their home-grown fans?

I expect that I'll be told in due course what's going on in Brian's mind.

Liverpool

Things have moved on a bit here and I'm poised to enter managerial classes. Yes, me! This very morning I was working in the NEMS office at Whitechapel, thinking vaguely about a pie and a pint at the pub round the corner. In walked Brian with a different proposition: "Alistair, let's have lunch, but first I'd like you to come with me to the Cavern Club."

"Sure, Brian" I agreed. "But why the Cavern?" God, I'm stupid sometimes.

"I want to hear the Beatles play and you told me they do lunchtime sessions at the Cavern."

So off we went, across Whitechapel and up the side streets until we turned into Mathew Street, which is a very narrow alleyway overshadowed by the old warehouses and generally looking like something out of the seamier side of a Charles Dickens novel. If Mathew Street looked uninviting, Brian's first view of the Cavern must have been positively underwhelming. All it is really is a converted cellar of one of the warehouses — and they didn't really bother to do very much in the way of conversion, either. There's a tiny doorway covered in names of bands and heart-throbs who have stirred the souls of the past audiences, all scratched on with a nail-file, and a big bouncer who stands at the door, looking to discourage any trouble before it enters. Quite the place for two sophisticated young businessmen in white shirts and dark suits to spend a civilized lunch!

From the racket coming up the stairs, it was clear that we'd missed the start of the session, so Brian paid two half-crowns to get us in and we negotiated the bouncer and went down the stairs.

The Cavern has a very fitting name. For a start, the ceiling arches over the dance-floor and drips condensation onto everyone, but nobody seemed to notice. There's very little lighting, but then there's nothing much worth looking at. But above all, it's crowded. There must have been 150 people packed into that tiny space, mainly teenagers. The girls wore the standard kit of short skirts, and beehive hair, but the boys were very much less fashionable, some even in working clothes. This is obviously where the young office workers go to dance away their lunchtimes! I only hope their bosses have no sense of smell, because the pong of cheap perfume, sweat and old tobacco was pretty nauseating to me, let alone the inexperienced nostrils of Brian.

Nevertheless, Brian and I felt horribly out of place in our business suits. I'm sure some of the lads thought we were police in plain clothes. All we wanted to do was find a table somewhere at the back and listen to the group, but there wasn't a table in sight. The audiences don't come here to eat or drink much, nor to chat each other up in subdued lighting round a romantic candle. They're only interested in the music. They must be — there isn't anything else!

Brian and I edged past the dancers, quite surprised when some of them greeted us. Of course, half our customers must come to the Cavern, and I recognized one or two people who'd bought "My Bonnie'. At last we found a couple of spare chairs near the back and could concentrate on the stage. I think that's a lie. It's not what anyone would call a stage, merely a few planks on some supports with a few token lights dimly illuminating the corners. It's so crowded on the dance floor that the group have to put their speakers at the back of the stage, but it doesn't seem to make much difference to the volume. The sound took out my eardrums and we had to shout directly at each other to make ourselves heard. I never thought that jazz was peaceful, but it is in comparison to this!

So, you ask, what are the Beatles like, after all this? The first thing that hit me was that they were four of the regular customers at NEMS, although they seem to spend more time listening to records than buying them. They're pretty sinister to look at — black leather trousers and jackets, black T-shirts and not another color to be seen. Also, Paul McCartney, the bass guitarist, is left-handed and that means that he and John Lennon, the rhythm player, often come together on stage for vocals with their guitars spread on either side like wings. The lead guitarist, George Harrison, spends most of the time fiddling with the controls on the amplifiers when he's not actually playing, while Pete Best, the drummer, sits grimly at the back, pounding out the beat.

As for their act, I don't think they'd go down very well at the Royal Variety Performance. It seems like they've got a permanent long-running set of private jokes which they share as they play. They crack one-liners to each other and from time to time let the front tow of the audience in on it. When the girls shouted requests, the Beatles shouted back, adding their own suggestions and comments on what the girls said. This wasn't the slick stage presence we might have expected from a group who could make the shop sell out of "My Bonnie" so often. Brian and I gave a discouraged look at each other and settled down to pay attention to the music.

This isn't much, I thought. For a start, it's too damned loud and from what I heard as we crossed the dance-floor, the Beatles are a bunch of five-chord merchants.

But no. Bloody awful their stage presence may be, crude their playing certainly was, but they've got something I can't describe and if I tried to write it down I'd have a wastepaper bin full of failed attempts and be no nearer telling you. All I can say is that I found my feet and fingers tapping as soon as I sat down, and when I stole a glance at Brian, I saw that his feet and fingers were going as much as mine!

But I didn't notice Brian very much after that; I was too excited and carried away by the music. "Sent" as we used to say.

We sat through five numbers, four of them standard beat songs: "Money', "Till There Was You', "A Taste of Honey" and "Twist and Shout'. I never heard standards like that played with the sort of raw excitement that the Beatles put into them. Then Paul McCartney came to the microphone and announced that they were going to play a song that he had written with John Lennon: "Hello Little Girl'. Brian and I exchanged a glance. So they write their own songs too.

And that was it. Suddenly it was all over, after twenty of the most mind-churning minutes I can remember. The Beatles said, "Thank you very much," took a round of applause and walked off the side of the stage to the dressing room. The audience began to drift away, most of them back to the offices and shops where they work, I suppose.

Brian had a certain gleam in his eye and he walked across to the dressing room, with me in close attendance. Even when we walked across the floor, we couldn't hear our footfalls, we were so deaf from the incredible noise those boys generate. At the dressing room door, Brian paused and knocked. "Come in," someone shouted.

We did. But we couldn't do more than poke our heads round into the broom cupboard that goes by the grand name of dressing room! The tiny space was full of Beatles wiping themselves down and replacing the liquid they'd sweated out during their set.

"Hello, I'm Brian Epstein and this is my Personal Assistant, Alistair Taylor."

"Hello," they replied, breathlessly. One of them remembered seeing us at NEMS.

"I just want to say we've seen your last five songs. You were great," Brian announced.

They looked a bit embarrassed. "Yeah, thanks."

Brian and I took our leave and walked across the dance-floor, which looked no bigger even when empty. In Mathew Street we took a deep breath of the fresh Mersey-laden air and sighed with relief that we were out of the thick atmosphere of the Cavern. How do people work in that sort of place day in, day out?

Neither of us broke the silence as we walked to a nearby restaurant called Peacock's. At least I don't think Brian said anything, but I probably wouldn't have heard him if he had, as my ears were ringing so much! Peacock's was a real haven of rest and peace after the Cavern.

When we were seated, Brian asked, "Well, Alistair, what do you think of the Beatles?"

"Brian, they look scruffy and they're not in the least professional...but they're absolutely tremendous!"

We caught each other's eye and burst out laughing. "They're tremendous, I agree, but how could anyone spend an hour or two in there?"

Over lunch we talked about our conversion, because converted we are. I've written often enough that I'm a jazz enthusiast and Brian's a classical man and neither of us has that much time for most pop music in our leisure hours. But the Beatles are something different and it only took them five songs to prove it to us. The other diners must have thought we were slightly cracked, as we kept laughing the whole time and I'm sure we were talking too loud because of our ringing ears!

Suddenly Brian stopped talking and leaned over the table with a serious expression. "Alistair, who do you work for? Me or NEMS?"

"You Brian, of course. Why do you ask me that?"

"Well, I'm thinking about managing the Beatles, but it would mean a lot of work and reorganization for us. I want to know what you think about the idea."

"It's fantastic. We certainly sell enough of their one record at the shop. Now we've seen what they're like on stage, I'm sure it's the only intelligent thing to do," I replied.

So this is what Brian has been leading up to, I thought. I should have realized a long time ago, but I never imagined him being involved in the sharp end of the music business. But what he went on to say proved that he's been thinking about this idea for weeks. We will have to have a separate company to manage the Beatles, as running the shops and managing a group would be too much for one man to handle.

Brian asked me, "If I start this new management company, I would like you to join me. What do you say to that, Alistair?"

"Ill work for you without a doubt, Brian," I answered. I will, too. I've never been so excited about a business idea in my life. We're going to be real babes in the wood at first, I thought. Even Brian doesn't know what a management contract looks like, but I expect his family solicitor can draw one up for us!

Then came Brian's bombshell: "Alistair, since you'll be very involved with the setting up and running of this new company, I'd like to give you two-and-a-half per cent of the Beatles" contract."

"Brian, I can't accept that, even though it's so generous. I've got no money of my own to put into the scheme and it'll cost a lot to set all of this up," I said.

"I don't want your money, just your loyalty," Brian persevered.

"Brian, you've already got my complete loyalty, you know that," I insisted. "All I need is a decent salary and I'll be happy."

So Brian let it drop. Have I done the right thing, I wonder? If the Beatles go on to be millionaires, I'm going to look a bit daft, aren't I? No, let those with the resources like Brian take the risk. I'll stay as I am.

So there we are. I'm now on the road to being a pop group manager — that is, if the Beatles will have us. We haven't asked them yet; we've hardly exchanged two words with them, in fact. They might not want us!

We didn't do much work this afternoon. Our minds are too full of what we might be about to set out on. It's all ifs and maybes, but both of us want to do this more than anything else we ever did.

2
CHAPTER

Liverpool

I've been totally snowed under with work in the last few weeks. It's not easy running a record store and breaking into pop group management! Lesley's now used to me coming in at all hours and falling instantly asleep, only to be up and away at crack of dawn.

Today hasn't been the best of days for me and Brian. We've spent all our spare time researching the past history of the Beatles and, you know Brian, he won't leave anything in doubt if he can make it more certain. I don't think there's anything about the Beatles that he hasn't wanted to know: were they born in Liverpool, how long have they played together, where have they played outside Liverpool, how long were they in Hamburg and what did they do there, do they play many of their own compositions, how reliable are they, and, of course, do they have any form of proper management (it doesn't look like it)?

You can guess who was asked to find out about that little lot. Yes, Detective Constable Taylor. Not that I mind; it's meant some very pleasant evenings nosing around the clubs and sniffing out information. I don't think that it's any secret that we want to manage the Beatles and there really doesn't seem to be any competition. From Brian's attitude, you'd think that they were going to be the finest beat group ever, but I suppose that's the way to start — as you mean to go on.

One thing's definitely true, though. The Beatles have amazing stage presence and talent. I've been to most of the regular beat venues listening to them and checking their act, with my copy of *Mersey Beat* tucked under my arm like any beat fan. God, I've sat through some rubbish. You wouldn't believe how hopeless some of the other bands are. I'm sure some of them play on five-stringed guitars. On the other hand, there's real talent around if you just look hard enough, but I don't expect any London managers can be bothered to come up to dreary old Liverpool to hear a new group. That's one of our secret fears — that someone will suddenly turn up and sign the Beatles before Brian's ready because, believe me, they've really got some quality that makes them stand out from the ranks of the groups like sunflowers in a rockery!

So after all this preparation, this was the day. Brian had asked the Beatles round to the NEMS offices at Whitechapel for a proper meeting. Now, when Brian sets a time for a meeting, it isn't a matter for negotiation. He always turns up on time and he expects everyone else to do the same. The only acceptable excuses are earthquakes and volcanic eruptions. Which was what we nearly had today.

The first to arrive was John Lennon, just about on time. I sat making small talk with him in the outer office until Pete Best and George Harrison turned up, much later. There was no sign of Paul McCartney, so I ushered three-quarters of the group into Brian's office, where he was sitting very tight and controlled. Nobody said anything for a while, then Brian suggested that one of the others should phone Paul's house. While George was dialling, I could see the tension and annoyance in Brian's hands as he tried not to let his anger show.

George put the phone down and turned to us, very embarrassed. "Paul's only just got up. He's in the bath."

I thought Brian was going to lay an egg, but instead of attacking the three who had managed to arrive, he just tersely said that he didn't want to discuss anything about management unless all four were there. We were dismissed, and the three Beatles went off somewhat crestfallen, doubtless to sort out Paul, or buy him an alarm clock.

If I wanted a group as much as Brian wants the Beatles, I think I'd have discussed management with one of their grannies over a milk-stout in the local. But Brian doesn't want that; everything, but everything, has to be perfectly cut and dried and he won't put up with second best. I can imagine I'll have to tell the Beatles that they're lucky to get a second chance.

If Paul ever gets rich enough to have a Rolls, we'll have to put a bath in the back!

Liverpool

It was second time lucky today as far as the Beatles were concerned. They'd obviously sorted themselves out and synchronized their watches, because this time they all showed up on the dot at the NEMS Whitechapel offices, late this afternoon.

It wasn't exactly one of those moments that shake the world. I took them through into Brian's inner office and we all sat down, very cramped. Here we were then, at last: the Beatles, their prospective manager and his Personal Assistant, all sitting on Brian's office furniture, wondering when we'll make our first million.

Brian doesn't like using his big office, which is upstairs, next to the other family offices, for these meetings with the Beatles. Instead we use what is really a stock room behind the shop. It's long and narrow, fitted with shelves and overflowing with records, catalogues and assorted stationery and office supplies. The only thing that makes it different is Brian's collection of bullfighting posters displayed on all the walls.

Anyway, here we were, sitting around Brian's tiny desk, waiting for him to set the ball in motion. He had a set talk all prepared and I could see that for once he was rather nervous. As he talked, though, he began to warm up and relax.

I was so keyed up that I can hardly remember his actual words: he explained to the Beatles that he would like to manage them, but he wasn't one hundred per cent sure what he can do for them at first. He was absolutely honest in saying he's never managed a group before, but they'll have to take his ability on trust. He did say that he thinks the group have real talent and he's got faith that they can go far in the music business, so why not give it a try?

Brian finished speaking and looked at the four Beatles, sitting on the uncomfortable office chairs. For a moment, nobody spoke, but they exchanged glances. Then John took the lead. He drew a deep breath and said, "Yes."

Paul, George and Pete at once chorused: "Yes. Manage us, please!"

"Yes!!!" This from John again, but yelled aloud!

Thank God for that, I thought. Here are Brian and I, sweating it out, worrying that they might say, "no', or "can we have some time to think about it?" and all they say is, "yes'. Not, "Yes, but', or, "Yes, if', but those sweet words, "Yes, Manage us, please." Perhaps they were thinking Brian was never going to ask them. Anyway, great sighs of relief all round.

So we're on our way. Brian's never seen a contract for a group before, so he's arranging for Rex Makin, his family solicitor, to draw up the contracts. When that's all ready, we're going to have another meeting at NEMS to go through all the paperwork and sign the mighty document. No wonder we were all grinning like schoolchildren when we left the office — Brian too!

Liverpool

Wednesday 13 December 1961 we signed the Beatles! We're part of the managerial classes now — next stop the London Palladium!

It's not been much of a day to remember in any other way. Dark, wet and cold, with a cutting wind blowing in from the Mersey. All the same, Brian and I were too excited to be bothered with anything but whether the Beatles would all turn up to the signing of the contracts — on time or not. Late in the afternoon, all four of them arrived together and came straight through into the inner office. There the contracts were laid out, only awaiting five signatures on each. I was to be the witness.

For once, the Beatles were quiet and respectful, like schoolboys unexpectedly invited in for tea by the teacher. If we see them as a big opportunity to succeed in show business, they for their part must see Brian as a real hot-shot young businessman. I think they are a little in awe at being asked to accept a manager, let alone the wealthy young man who has made such a success of NEMS.

Brian quietly asked them to sign the contracts and in turn they took up the pen to write their signatures over four of the five sixpenny stamps. Never was a peace treaty signed so quietly: J. W. Lennon, George Harrison, James Paul McCartney, R.P. Best. After each had signed, I witnessed the signature: "in the presence of J.A. Taylor'. All that was now needed was Brian's signature and my signature as witness to it.

Then Brian dropped his bombshell. "I'm not going to sign the contract."

The mood in the room changed suddenly, from mounting excitement and glee to confusion and anxiety. None of us had any idea what this meant. Brian certainly hadn't mentioned anything about it to me. Could he be backing out?

Brian at once gave us an explanation, but I'm still not sure that I understand it. Maybe I'm not very bright, but I can't see the reasoning behind it at all. He said that he hadn't signed the contract because he didn't want the Beatles to feel tied to him in any way. If they want to sack him, they can do so at any time, without any legal difficulties. On the other hand, he said, his word is his bond and he doesn't need to sign a piece of paper to prove it. This way, they can have all the benefits of being professionally managed, without any of the legal obligations. Then came the even more bizarre bit: he asked me to witness the non-signing of the contract by Brian Epstein. Well, he's the boss, and I suppose he's got his reasons for doing this, but it seems to me that a contract isn't a contract at all unless it's signed by both parties. I signed, and for some reason added my address to fill the empty space!

After this short panic, our heartbeats began to return to normal and Brian gave his first speech as the manager of the Beatles. All pep talks are more or less the same, but Brian was out to impress on the boys that there are a few things he wants done — his way.

The first thing Brian says he wants is a recording contract. He says he's got a lot of contacts in the record business from his years running NEMS and that he'll set to work at once to arrange a deal. For their part, the Beatles are to stop acting like a bunch of amateurs, and transform themselves into a tight professional-looking group. Brian set out the rules as if he were a teacher talking to a group of new boys: "I want you all to make yourselves a lot smarter in appearance. On stage there must be no drinking, no smoking, no chewing gum and, especially, no swearing. The audience isn't there to talk to you, so don't chat to the pretty girls while you're on stage. Be punctual. If you're scheduled to arrive at a certain time, make sure you arrive when you're meant to. Remember that you're professionals now, with a reputation to keep."

Brian's attitude to professionalism goes further than this. Tomorrow he's going to take the Beatles over to a tailor in Birkenhead to have made-to-measure suits ordered. Also on the shopping list are haircuts, shirts, ties, shoes — the lot. Brian must have noticed the odd look that the boys passed between each other, because he asked, "Do you have any objections to these plans?" The answer was a great big "no'; they're happy to go along with anything that Brian wants, if it increases their chances of becoming stars. Besides, Brian said he'll pay for all this!

I think the Beatles must think they've hit the big time already, because some of Brian's next remarks made them sound as if half the record companies are after them! He doesn't want them to be bothered about anything else but their performance and their music. That's their side of the deal. His side is the business, and he doesn't want them to be involved in that at all. Any requests for appearances from agents, promoters or ballroom managers must be answered with "please talk to our manager about it'. Brian has promised to handle all their booking arrangements, go to all their shows and act as their agent and financial manager in every detail.

"Every detail" includes me. Each week, the Beatles, Neil Aspinall, their equipment manager, and I are to be given a statement of the next week's schedule, including dates and times of appearances, venues, number of sets to be played and length of each, pay rates and so on and so on. They'll each receive a statement of their earnings, along with the cash. I know who's going to be doing most of this organizing!

Through all of this, the Beatles sat drinking in every word and looking at Brian as if he was going to lead them to the end of the rainbow. His final words were that he's eventually going to take them to the top, yes, to London. He's convinced they're going to be world famous.

At this, they all grinned and looked a bit embarrassed, like most of us English do when singled out for praise. But there came a voice from the back of the cramped group: "I hope we're all going to be stars, but I'll tell you one thing. Whether we make it as a group or not, I'm going to be a star!" Paul McCartney looked round at us with a gleam in his eye as he finished talking, then burst out laughing with the rest of us.

A good way to bring the meeting to a close! Brian went off with the Beatles to the Casbah Club for his first dose of management, while I slipped off home, because Lesley and I have to go out to dinner tonight.

Somehow, I don't think I'm going to have time for much social life in the months ahead. Lesley's going to have to get used to being the wife of a show business man! Brian really means what he says about going to London, and he's already told me some of his plans. NEMS seems to have slipped from the top of his pile of priorities and he's going to stake all on this group. Having heard some of their sets at the Cavern, I can see Why we wants to take the risk. What a world we might be opening up, if we don't go bust on the way!

Liverpool

Day two of our managerial status, but still no Rolls-Royce has turned up at the office, the pavements are still made of slippery stone and the sky's too cloudy to manage a rainbow! It doesn't matter — we're on our way to the top and everything feels different. When Brian talked to us yesterday, I felt that it was all an incredible dream, but we might just make it. In the grey light of a Mersey dawn, it looks even more unlikely that we'll end up at the London Palladium, but what the hell, let's give it a go.

Brian was already in the office when I arrived this morning and from the amount of work that he'd already got through he must have come in at about six o'clock. All the paperwork for the ordinary retail business of NEMS had been taken care of and he was at his desk typing a memo containing all that we had talked about last night. Everything was there: the signing, the reasons for Brian's non-signature, the pep talk and the terms of the contract. There's going to be no lack of thoroughness in this operation, thought I. Better put my alarm clock forward an hour.

Last night, Brian told us how much he wants to get a recording contract for the boys; without that they might as well resign themselves to playing in grotty little clubs and ballrooms for the rest of their lives. The recording contract will launch them into the big time, especially if they can manage a hit bell on *Juke Box Jury*. Now Brian's pretty sure that he's got all the right contacts to break into the recording world — after all, he must be the biggest record retailer in Liverpool and all the record companies know about his ability to smell out the hits. One look at their orders from NEMS will show them that time after time Brian orders large quantities of records by unknown artistes who go on to score big hits in the charts; just as importantly, there have been lots of records by established artistes which Brian hasn't ordered in great bulk and which haven't been hits. We really don't think that landing a recording contract, or at least an audition, will be any great problem.

Brian's mind was running along the same lines as mine this morning because as soon as he'd finished typing the memo he rang up half a dozen of his best contacts in the record companies. Sod's Law of course ruled that they were all out. Anyway, he asked their secretaries to arrange for them to ring him back as soon as they could. Ball number one was now rolling very well and it was time to set everything else in motion.

It's ages since I went across the Mersey on the ferry. It always brings back memories of bucket and spade days with the family on New Brighton beach and I'm overwhelmed by the urge to dig canals in the sand and go for a donkey ride. Today's ferry across the Mersey was strictly business, though, and a good job too, in the middle of December! We were on our way to see Brian's tailor and have the Beatles measured for matching suits.

When the boys turned up, we set off for the ferry. They were still dressed in their leathers, still as scruffy as ever, while Brian and I were in our usual dark suits and overcoats. What a sight we must have looked — like two plain-clothes policemen escorting some dangerous villains! On the ferry trip the boys began to relax in our company for the first time. We've all only properly met before on each others territory, either at the Cavern or at the NEMS offices. Now, on the ferry, feeling the sea breeze on our faces and staring at the old, familiar Liverpool sights- - ships tied up at the pier, Liver building growing distant behind us — we felt more of a unit. John and the others kept up a string of private jokes, while Brian and I listened, gradually beginning to understand what some of them were about.

It's only about a quarter of an hour's trip on the ferry to Birkenhead, but it was our first trip with the Beatles — first of many, I hope! We walked about half a mile to Brian's tailor, the boys acting really excited at the thought of having proper made-to-measure suits. The tailor's shop is a very traditional place, with nothing but shelves filled with great bolts of material from floor to ceiling and a couple of dummies in one corner. No off the peg stuff here, I thought. The tailor himself is a little bald Jewish man, and obviously a great friend of Brian. He greeted us all very warmly and he and Brian went into a huddle over books of cloth samples.

Brian obviously had everything worked out in advance, because it only took him about ten minutes to select a fabric and pattern. The Beatles are to take flight in dark blue suits, quite a bit different from their usual black leather.

Once the fabric had been selected, the next step was for the tailor to take the measurements of John, Paul, George and Pete. This usually takes hours and Brian and the tailor seemed prepared to spend all day if necessary. Here's where we'll have trouble, I thought, eyeing John, who seems to be the natural rebel. But no! The Beatles are happy to wear anything Brian selects for them, as long as it brings them that much nearer to success.

In the end, it didn't take long and the tailor asked Brian when they could come again for a fitting. Brian explained why we want these suits and just asked for them as soon as possible. He looks the sort of craftsman who'll be up half the night getting the seams exactly right. There certainly won't be a neater band on the shores of the Mersey!

Next it was back to Liverpool on the ferry, with the boys laughing and chattering about their new suits and about how rich we are all going to be when we hit the big time. I caught Brian's eye, and he grinned, as if the say, "You'd better believe it."

The rest of today I spent back on the counter at NEMS, catching up on half a morning's work and trying to keep my feet on the ground. Brian's mellow mood was a bit disturbed when he found that none of the record companies had called him back, although he asked them to this morning. Early days yet, I suppose.

Tomorrow the Beatles are off with Brian to collect the rest of their outfits and have their hair cut. I'm to watch the shop and take any phone calls from the record companies. It's really been a day and a half for me, and I'll be glad to sink into a hot bath and put my feet up for the rest of the evening.

Liverpool

For all my optimism, the only contact I've had with the national newspapers recently has been around the fish and chips that I've been eating in five snatched minutes at lunchtime. Life here is very hectic now that we've got two businesses to run, and much of the day-to-day activity of the NEMS shop has been in my hands for the last week or two.

Brian is giving all his energy to launching the Beatles — you wouldn't think anything else was important to him. The day after we ordered the suits (which have now arrived — very smart, too), he took the boys out to Horne Brothers to have their hair cut in the style he demands. I have the feeling that the Beatles weren't too pleased about the prospect of a visit to the barber. They needn't have worried. Horne Brothers are a very classy hairdressers — none of your pudding basin shearing job and sticking your ear back on with Elastoplast there!

When they all returned at lunchtime, the Beatles still had long hair (to their relief), but it's now been neatly trimmed and styled and the greasy appearance has been replaced by a sleek well-maintained look. The rest of the morning was spent in the man's outfitters of Liverpool, to judge by the parcels they came back carrying. Each of them wanted to unwrap his parcel and show off the new clothes, and for half an hour it was like Christmas a week or two early. Each one had new shirts, ties (which will take some getting used to at first), and boots. There's nothing too conservative or square, but everything's selected with Brian's eye for style and color. I'm sure he enjoyed the shopping trip as much as any of them and I know that he doesn't mind paying for all these changes. He regards it all as an excellent investment and he's even said that he doesn't want any of the usual manager's commission until the Beatles are fully established. There's confidence for you!

So the boys now feel that they're becoming a professional outfit in both senses of the word. They spent the rest of their visit to the office talking about their glowing future as if they really believe that they're on their way. Things weren't quite so rosy when the boys had left, though. Brian was already put out because the record companies still hadn't rung him back. He was even more frustrated and irritable when he made all the calls again and found that he still couldn't contact anyone. After the last of half a dozen calls, he slammed the phone down and said, "If these people don't send someone down here to listen to the Beatles, then I'll stop all my orders for records from them. That'll make them take notice." It takes quite a lot to shock me, but I'm very worried that Brian seems willing to put the record business at NEMS on the line for the Beatles so quickly. There must be other ways to meet the right people, and I'm sure he'll find a way soon. I hope he does, because he's becoming very frustrated and tense at being ignored. After all, he is the oracle of the Liverpool record world!

Managing a pop group isn't just a matter of buying clothes and phoning record companies. I found that out on that second afternoon, when Brian and I went through the business arrangements. We have set aside a small area in the back office purely for Beatles paperwork. Brian has bought a big desk diary which we're going to use to keep a record of all the bookings the boys have and all the other meetings and sessions which we will set up. This is now sitting in solitary state on the desk top, with hundreds of creamy white pages just waiting to be filled in: Cavern Club...London Palladium...Royal Variety Performance.... To keep our feet firmly on the ground, Brian also has presented all of us with a copy of a memo he typed yesterday morning, the school rules: no drinking, smoking, stupidity or chatting up girls on stage, clean and tidy appearance, professional behavior at all times and don't be late for anything.

Liverpool

Brian has been in the shop less and less. All his time is being taken up by the Beatles, who are beginning to learn what a hard character he can be. That precise and polite exterior conceals the instincts of a hunter, always on the look out for what he wants. At the moment, what Brian wants above all else is a recording contract for the boys, but he hasn't yet managed to interest anyone enough to agree even to turn up for an audition.

What Brian can organize is a full list of bookings. Lewis Buckley and Sam Leach, two of the biggest names in promotion around here, have been feeling the weight of Brian's onslaught and the result's been a healthy increase in the number of Beatles gigs. Brian goes to everything that the Beatles do, however small. Every arrangement is discussed in advance so that they all know exactly when and where they are due to turn up; every concert finds Brian quietly sitting out of the bright lights, observing and thinking about improvements in the presentation — but never the music. It is Brian who negotiates the fee, and it's Brian's hard-headed dealing which is gradually pulling bigger appearance money for the boys. It is Brian who collects their money at the end of the night and works out the division of the loot. It's also Brian who pays all their expenses while taking nothing for himself — not out of charity, he insists, but because he sees the Beatles being a success for years to come. If they ask him when he'll want his share, he just replies that he'll worry about that when the Beatles are nationally successful. The way he says that always make me believe that it's going to happen.

Even for Brian, there are only twenty-four hours in a day, seven days in a week. NEMS is being just a little neglected, if you call being left in my capable hands neglect! Much of the ordinary business of the shop is now handled by me, although Brian still does all the ordering of records. It's as if he were one of those characters who spin dozens of plates on the end of long poles at the circus. He'll dash in, give NEMS a quick flick to keep everything spinning, then be off at high speed to the Beatles business before its plate falls off the pole. Most of the plate-spinning acts only last for five minutes, but Brian has only just started.

Liverpool

It's cold enough to freeze the legs off a brass Beatle! At the moment, it sometimes feels as if we're stuck two rungs up from the bottom of the ladder. There's an awful lot of hard work for everyone, especially Brian, but we're just keeping on, despite all the problems which we didn't foresee.

The biggest difficulty is arranging for an audition for a recording contract. It seems that neither of us knows the ins and outs of the record industry as well as we thought we did. All Brian's contacts are in the wholesale and retail end of the business and we've found out from bitter experience that they have nothing at all to do with the people who search for new talent. The talent spotters are called Artist and Repertoire, A&R for short. That's why all his calls to the record companies have been ignored.

Brian's slowly becoming frustrated enough with the logjam to threaten to do something drastic unless someone sends an A&R man to hear the Beatles. He spends most of the time he's at NEMS in the office telephoning and not getting very far. I think he'll really threaten them with stopping all NEMS orders if he doesn't come up with an audition soon.

Family tensions are also putting a strain on Brian at the moment. From the conversations I've had with him over the months, I've gathered that the only thing he's ever made a really big success of is NEMS. His schooldays weren't very happy and National Service was even grimmer for him than it was for the rest of us, since he's so fastidious and sensitive. Even his few terms at drama college ended in his preferring to leave and come back to the family business. Building up the record retailing side of NEMS has been his major achievement. As you'd expect, Harry and Queenie, Brian's father and mother, are becoming a little concerned that he's letting the NEMS business coast along while he's giving his attention to the Beatles, whom they must see as just another beat group. They see Brian's money being poured out on new suits and other clothes, transport costs, phone bills and entertainment, while there doesn't seem to be any return on his investment. They made a success out of selling furniture and I don't think they're very happy that their son is in such a high-risk business.

Lately, Brian's father has taken to coming into the office to check up on the running of the shop. He's very like Brian in many ways, a tall man, handsome and always immaculately turned out. Underneath his charming and polite exterior lurks the same hunter's instinct as Brian has.

It's difficult to be evasive with him, especially when he asks searching questions about the business: "Alistair, are the record stocks sufficient this week?"

"Alistair, did you order enough copies of that record?"

"Alistair, are the staff being managed adequately?"

"Alistair, could you tell me just exactly where Brian is, please?"

The only effect all of this has on Brian is to make him even more determined to succeed, but I can understand Harry's point. Four scruffy musicians playing for fifteen pounds a night can't seem much when weighed in the balance against a whole business. But then, Harry hasn't seen the Beatles perform....

The other night I went to see the Beatles for the first time since we signed the contracts. It seems incredible that I haven't gone earlier, but life's been so hectic trying to keep everything running at NEMS. I went over the river to New Brighton, where the boys were playing at the Tower Ballroom. Now the Tower's no small booking; it's an enormous hall which takes over a thousand people. Definitely the place to be seen. The Beatles were sharing the bill with three other local groups: Rory Storm and the Hurricanes, Derry and the Seniors and Dale Roberts and the Jaywalkers.

There's just no competition. The Beatles were absolutely phenomenal. Now that Brian's made them smarten up and put a little bit of order into the way they do things, they act like a top professional band. It even seems to have added something to their music; confidence, I suppose. It's an old cliche to say they took the place by storm, but as far as most of the audience was concerned there need not have been any other group on the bill.

Brian and I shared a table at the side while the boys performed, and we found ourselves unable to stop grinning at each other during their set. If Brian's parents could see the pride that he takes in the Beatles and the concern that he feels for them, they'd feel much happier about the whole project, I'm sure.

When the set was over, Brian leaned across to me and said, "Alistair, soon the Beatles will be too big for Liverpool. We'll be going to set up in London."

"What, a bank from Liverpool making it in London, Brian? We both know they're the best group we ever heard, but how will they fare down South?"

"They'll love them."

"Absolutely right, Brian."

\When the boys had put their gear back in the dressing room, they came over to have a few well-deserved drinks with us. Brian bought a round, then I stumped up for another. We were just finishing these drinks when John tapped on my knee. I leaned across to him and he whispered into my ear, "Can you lend us a couple of quid, Al?" The Beatles are broke!

I discreetly slipped two pounds under the table to him and he winked his thanks. It's all right for Brian to buy clothes and pay for all the travelling, but drinking's different. No one likes not to be able to stand a round, especially someone as independent as John.

Pay me back when you're a millionaire, mate, say in a year or two!

Liverpool

Yesterday I nearly got the sack from Brian. Perhaps I'm not made of the stuff of good Personal Assistants, but I don't feel it was entirely my fault.

The other morning, Brian came into the office at NEMS and told me that he was going to be away on business all day. I was to handle all his telephone calls, as well as run the shop. Well, I'm getting used to Brian being away for long periods of time trying to arrange recording contracts for the boys, so I told him not to worry; I'd mind the store.

Brian couldn't have been gone five minutes when I heard the phone in his office ring. Great, I thought, as I threaded my way through the shop and out to the back office, why don't we have a phone at the counter? Still, the call was good news — a booking for the Beatles. I glanced through Brian's big desk diary and saw that there was nothing already booked. "That'll be fine. Just send us the contracts for the booking and we'll have them to you by return."

The first trouble came when I tried to find a pen. Blast, I'd left it in the shop. All I had was a pencil, so I thought I had better write down all the information about the booking on to a scrap of paper rather than into the diary. Brian doesn't like scruffy pencilled notes in the official diary. In the middle of all this, Josie Balmer, the shop manager, rushed into the office, saying, "Alistair, there's a huge queue at the counter. Can you help our, please?"

I thrust the scrap of paper into my pocket and rushed out into the shop. It was like the Tower of Babel out there. Not only was it the school holidays, it was also wet, and that meant that half of the local kids were in the shop listening to records. There was a snake of teenagers all waiting to hear their favorites, most without much intention of buying. But that doesn't matter. A customer is a customer, and where would we be if we'd ignored Raymond Jones?

The noise was appalling. Several records were playing at once in different areas of the shop — and none of them was quiet! Most of them sounded as if they were made by Anna Deane and the Phensics, the thumping was so loud. My head wasn't in the best condition as it was, because I'd been up late at the Beatles performance the night before, but the racket in the shop finished if off. No time for lunch, of course, just a couple of aspirins washed down with a glass of water.

On a day like that Sod's Law rules that the telephone will never stop ringing. Every call meant a rush through to the back office, and so I was on the go all afternoon. Towards closing time I took a call from another promoter — yet another booking for the Beatles. We're coming up in the world, I thought. I looked in the diary and there was nothing there, so I accepted the offer and wrote the details down in the diary. "Fine, please send us the contracts...."

Brian came into the shop just before closing time, and just before my own imminent collapse!

"How are things, Alistair?"

"Middling to dreadful, Brian, but good for trade. It's been like Clapham Junction here — not a minute's break all day. Oh yes, there's a booking for the boys; I put it into the desk diary."

"Good. You look absolutely shattered. Go on home and put your feet up."

I didn't need him to ask twice. I was out of the door in two minutes.

This morning I turned up at NEMS to find Brian opening his mail, as usual. Off I went to the counter and I was happily working away when Brian came up to me and hissed, "Alistair, I want to see you in my office at once." He had that carefully controlled look which comes over him when he's angry, so I left everything and followed him to the back office, wondering what was wrong.

There were two contracts laid out on Brian's desk. He stood behind the desk and pointed to them as if they were my death warrants. "Alistair, these are two contracts which came to me this morning from different promoters. They're both for the same night at clubs which are fifteen miles apart! The Beatles cannot possible fulfil both bookings! What explanation can you give me which might prevent me asking for your resignation?"

I looked at the contracts. Surely I'd never done anything so stupid. Then I remembered I'd written down the details of the first booking on the piece of paper and forgotten to transfer them to the desk diary. The second booking was the one I'd written in. I fished into my pocket and found the crumpled piece of scrap paper. "Well, Brian, it's like this..."

Brian was considerably less than impressed. His voice was shaking with rage as he delivered the most stinging lecture I've had since I left school.

"Do you realize that our professional reputation as managers depends on keeping our word and fulfilling our bookings? How can we expect anyone to take us seriously if we act like clowns? Everything has to be done properly and I will accept no excuses. What you did has cast a shadow on the reputation not only of me but also of the Beatles. It's up to you to remedy the situation at once; your job depends on it!"

Oh God, it was not use pointing out that I'd been too busy to think straight. Brian just does not tolerate inefficiency of that sort. Apologies were not substitute for action, so I picked up the phone and dialled the number of one of the promoters.

"Hello, Alistair Taylor of NEMS here. I'm afraid we've run into a little difficulty with that booking for the Beatles. Someone in the office had already accepted a booking for that night and hadn't put it into the diary. Is there any chance of changing it to another night soon? I'm terribly sorry to inconvenience you like this."

"Oh, that's all right," came the reassuring voice at the other end. "We're used to double bookings. Most of the managers do it at some time or another. Don't worry about it; we'll get another band for that night and fix up a time for the Beatles to play when they're free. The kids probably won't notice; "all the bands around here sound the same, anyway."

I could have kissed him down the line, even if I didn't think much of his musical taste. Back to Brian I went, rather unsure of my reception. My legs were actually trembling as I went up to him, just like a naughty child waiting to be beaten.

It was all right. Now that he'd relieved himself of his feelings, Brian was in a much calmer frame of mind. He was even pleased at how speedily everything had been sorted out. This was my chance to unburden myself of all my anxieties about running the shop while he's away. I told him what a strain it was (but didn't say anything about his father's attitude to the Beatles) and even offered to resign if he didn't think I was up to the job.

It's unbelievable! Brian was so charming and pleasant, I could hardly believe that he'd been shaking with suppressed rage not ten minutes earlier. "All right, Alistair. I don't want your resignation. In fact, you're essential to the running of the whole project and I'm sorry if I've been overloading you. I hope it won't be for too long, because I intend to break out of Liverpool and move to London as soon as possible. With your help, I want to put the Beatles at the top of the music business. But remember, no more mistakes!"

Oh no, there'll be no more mistakes. I don't want the sack and I know Brian means it. I couldn't ever go back to being a clerk in a timber importer's office again!

Liverpool

Brian and I have parted company. I never really thought it could happen, but I didn't bargain for Lesley's asthma becoming so bad that the doctor has advised her to live in a drier climate than the misty north-west. There was really nothing else to do but look around for a job in the south of England as quickly as possible. I was lucky enough to be offered a job with Pye Records in London, but the trouble was that they wanted me to start in a week's time.

My contract with NEMS allowed me to leave after a week's notice, but I was terribly upset to realize that Brian was away on business in Germany when I handed in my notice to Clive Epstein, Brian's brother. It seemed so sneaky and underhand to give in my notice while Brian was away. Clive was running things in Brian's absence, and I explained to him that if I didn't take up the job with Pye as soon as I could, they wouldn't hold it open for me. Fair enough, Clive said, Lesley's health must come first. It was too important to chance a delay.

Brian returned from Germany today, just as I was settling all my NEMS business and clearing my desk. Clive had already told him that I was about to leave and he was furious. He came storming in and physically shoved me into his office. How could I walk out like that without giving longer notice? How could I leave him in the lurch to run everything on his own? Had I no loyalty, did grooming the Beatles for stardom and finding them a recording contract mean nothing to me?

I tried to explain that I had no real choice but to leave the area, but there was no arguing with Brian in that mood. He just wouldn't listen to a word I said. At last I just walked out of his office, picked up my coat and left.

So there we are. No more stories about the making of a pop group, no more little Beatle souvenirs. I'm not so vain as to think that they won't make good without me, though! I'm going to do all I can to make the people in London take Brian and the Beatles seriously, because they need that one big break. Even in the last few days before he left for Germany, Brian was still on the same endless round of phone calls. still waiting for people to phone him back. There was a guy called George Martin due to phone him, but Brian was waiting almost with tears in his eyes as the days went past and his call still had not been returned.

John, strumming his guitar at Magic Alex's house, Athens, 1968. (Alistair Taylor)

3

CHAPTER

London

I'm back with the Beatles again! Yesterday I had lunch with Brian, of all people, and he's invited me to become General Manager of NEMS Enterprises. That's the management company he's formed to look after the Beatles and all the other acts he's taking on!

I've been very bored at Pye in the last few months and as the Beatles shot into the stratosphere of fame I've been wondering how different things might have been if I'd stayed with Brian. Certainly I wouldn't have spent 1963 working in an office like Pye. I'd made a bit of a name for myself in the office before the Beatles released "Love Me Do" and it all started happening by going on about this fabulous group from Liverpool and how they were sure to be a marvelous success. When they finally hit the charts at the end of last year, I couldn't really disguise the told-you-so look on my face!

Anyway, the result of all this was that everyone at Pye knew that I'd once worked for Brian Epstein. I hadn't seen Brian since that last awful row in Liverpool, but gradually people at the office started to say, "Oh, I saw your ex-boss in here yesterday." It turned out that Tommy Quickly, who's one of Brian's new artistes, has been signed for the Pye International record label and that Brian was coming down from Liverpool quite often to make all the necessary arrangements. I had no thought of asking Brian for a job, but it did strike me that he might be prepared to give me a reference and that a recommendation from a household name like him would count for a lot in my efforts to escape from Pye. With this in mind, I asked everyone to tell Brian the next time that they saw him that I'd appreciate a word with him. I really didn't know whether he'd even talk to me, but it seemed too good a chance to pass by.

A couple of weeks ago, I was walking down the corridor at Pye reading something from a piece of paper. All the way down this corridor are the executives" offices, each with a secretary's desk outside. Standing with his back to me next to one of the desks was a guy in a checked overcoat talking on the telephone. As I drew closer to him, he put the telephone down, turned round and bumped into me. I stepped back quickly.

"I'm terribly sorry. I . . .Brian!"

"Alistair!" he beamed. "How good to see you. How are things going?"

"Fine," I grinned, pleased that Brian seemed to have forgotten the way we'd parted.

Before I could say any more, Brian carried on, "Look, we've got to have lunch together. I can't possibly do it today, as I'm heading off back to Liverpool, but drop me a line and let me know when you can come to lunch with me."

It was so good to see him again; of course I agreed.

NEMS ENTERPRISES LTD

DIRECTORS: B. AND C. J. EPSTEIN

24 MOORFIELDS, LIVERPOOL, 2 TELEPHONE CENtral 0793

Reference BE/DW

30th September, 1963.

Dear Alistair (well I am in show biz now!),

Thank you for your letter of the 24th. Indeed it was a pleasure to see you again at Pye last week. How about lunch on Monday, October 7th, 1963. If you like we could eat at the Cumberland which would be convenient for both of us. If you can manage this, perhaps we could meet in the bar of the grill (that's downstairs) at say 1.0 p.m.

Looking forward to hearing from you.

Yours sincerely,
BRIAN EPSTEIN

A. Taylor, Esq.,
48 Thurleigh Court,
Nightingale Lane,
LONDON, S.W.12.

Service Agreement dated **25th January, 1965.**

between

NEMS ENTERPRISES LTD.,
23 ALBEMARLE STREET,
LONDON, W.1. ("the Company")

and

JAMES ALISTAIR TAYLOR

("the Employee")

The Company engages the Employee and the Employee agrees to serve the Company as **GENERAL MANAGER** on the following terms and conditions:—

* 1. **TERM:** **1 YEAR, 9 MONTHS** ~~years~~ from the date of this agreement. Unless then terminated by the Company by thirty days written notice the engagement shall continue thereafter subject to termination by either party at any time on thirty days notice.

2. **SALARY:** £1550 per annum payable monthly at the end of each calendar month.

3. **HOLIDAYS: THREE** weeks per year with full pay at such times as may be convenient to both parties.

4. **ABSENCE** caused by illness, etc: The Company may determine this agreement without notice if through illness or other justifiable cause the Employee is absent from his duties for an aggregate of six weeks in any fifty-two consecutive weeks. Until such determination the Employee shall be paid full salary for the first four weeks' absence and fifty per cent of salary thereafter. The Employee shall not be required to account for any monies received under the National Insurance Act, 1946 in respect of illness.

   In case of illness a doctor's certificate shall be produced to the Company in respect of any absence of more than two days duration.

5. **DISMISSAL** for breach of regulations, etc: The Company may at all times dismiss the Employee without notice on grounds of breach of the Company's regulations or other improper conduct.

6. **GENERAL TERMS**

   a) The Employee shall comply with all reasonable and proper instructions and directions of the Company and attend punctually at such places as his duties may require and devote his whole time and attention to the business of the Company during the Company's usual business hours.

   b) The Employee will not during the continuance of his employment by the Company be concerned in any manner whatsoever with any other business similar to that of the Company unless any such business activity has been specifically authorized by the Company.

   c) The Employee will not divulge to any person or persons during or after the period of this engagement any information coming to his knowledge during this engagement concerning the Company's business or clients or communicate with (except on the Company's business) or solicit any clients of the Company.

Signed For and on Behalf of the Company

DIRECTOR

Accepted and Agreed to

The Employee

* **Employment commenced 25th October, 1963.**

Our first appointment was to meet at the grill at the Cumberland Hotel, opposite the Pye buildings on the corner of Marble Arch. Brian couldn't make that, however, and we ended up meeting at Bentley's Restaurant in Swallow Street. We spent the entire excellent luncheon with each of us blaming himself for the row! I was apologizing for not being able to give him more notice; Brian was asking my forgiveness for the way he'd lost his temper with me.

The end product of the meeting was that I've been appointed General Manager of NEMS Enterprises and that I'm going to give a week's notice to Pye! Brian hasn't changed. When I first was interviewed by him, he had me arranging that very afternoon for his bullfighting prints to be framed. Well, this time he said, "I've taken this incredible new flat in William Mews in Belgravia. This afternoon I'm gong off to choose the carpets. I want you to come with me and help me."

"But I'm expected back in the office at Pye," I protested.

"Oh, that'll be all right. I'll explain everything to them. You're with me now."

So the morning had seen me as a lowly clerk at Pye and by the afternoon I was a General Manager — whatever that's going to mean! Pye didn't see me for the rest of the day, I'm afraid, and this morning I received a letter which Brian must have posted as soon as he arrived home. It said what a great lunch we'd had and confirmed my appointment. There was a PS: "Don't forget about the carpet underlay."

London

Things are moving very quickly for me now that I'm back working with Brian. He came up to me this morning and said, "Alistair, I've told the boys that you're back with us and they're really pleased. They're playing at the East Ham Granada tonight. They'd love to see you again and it'll be a baptism of fire into Beatlemania for you!" Fine, I said. I'll be there. Suddenly I thought of the date. November the fifth — Bonfire Night. I hoped it wasn't an omen!

So off I went to the East End of London, to find the East Ham Granada besieged by an army of Beatle fans. Now, I've seen them on television, but in the flesh they're totally different — the noise, the pushing and shoving, the sheer emotion of it all is really more than a bit frightening especially when looking after the creators of all the rumpus is going to be my responsibility! It felt like a victory even to make it to the boys" dressing room in one piece.

Once there, it was the same old Beatles who were laughing and joking before they went on stage. They're a little more self-assured, perhaps, but really no different. They greeted me as if I'd just been over the road to buy a packet of fags. It was as if I'd never been away for my little excursion to work for Pye. Good to be back, indeed.

One thing has changed. Pete Best has been replaced by Ringo Starr since I saw the Beatles. I was sorry to hear from Brian the tale of how the other Beatles had come to him and said they wanted a different drummer; it must have been hard for Peter to have gone through all the years of coffee bars and assembly halls, only to find himself shunted out just as the Beatles have become the most exciting act in show business. Still, I always did say to Brian that I thought Pete's drumming was a touch uneven, that somehow he didn't quite fit into the group.

I think Brian was sad when it was put to him that Pete had to go, but he has offered him another group. I hope Pete makes it on his own in some way. To be cast off as an ex-Beatle must be very lonely. On the other hand, Ringo seems to have settled in straight away, and he provides the others with a very professional framework of rhythm.

There were other new faces in the dressing room, new to me at any rate. A scriptwriter called Alun Owen was there, discussing with the boys some ideas for the script of a film they're going to make for release next summer.

After a few minutes, the door opened and in walked George Martin, the producer who's had so much to do with the success of the Beatles" records. It was the first time I'd met him, but I remember well Brian anxiously waiting for a phone call from George, back in the days when we were praying for a recording contract. He held up his hand for silence and announced, "Listen, everybody. I've got something important to tell you all. I've just heard the news from EMI that the advance sales of "I Want To Hold Your Hand" have topped the one million mark. That's the first time that's ever happened!"

We raised the roof for minutes on end with cheering and back-slapping. If the fans outside had kept quiet, they'd probably have heard us. When it all died down, John said in a mocking tone, "Yeah, great. But that means it'll only be at Number One for about a week." You can't satisfy some people!

Anyway, I expect he's wrong about that. There are people buying Beatles records who've never bought a record before in their lives!"

All I heard of the Beatles" actual performance was a few guitar chords, the odd extra loud thump from Ringo's bass drum and the mass screaming of thousands of strained female larynxes.

The screaming was utterly deafening and my ears are still ringing from it. In fact, I retreated from my place in the wings to one of the dressing rooms to get my breath back, like a battle-shocked sailor trying to escape into the bowels of a man-of-war. The whole thing was as shocking, violent and exciting as standing at the end of a breakwater during a gale. The noise and the emotion of it all is completely overwhelming.

I'm glad I'm not a member of Peter Jay's Jaywalkers or the Brooks Brothers. Whatever they do, however good they are, they're not going to make any impression on the thousands of fans who come only to see the Beatles and to hear the sound of their own screaming in overdrive.

Strangest of all were the memories that came flooding back of seeing the Beatles play that first lunch time at the Cavern, years ago; watching their pleasure at being taken shopping by Brian in and at the Tower Ballroom in New Brighton and of joking about them one day appearing at the London Palladium and the Royal Variety Performance — both of which they've just done! I just can't yet believe that they were playing in front of the Queen Mother and Princess Margaret only last night. Do you think the Royal Family gave the odd polite scream? How many more of my fantasies are going to come true?

Some things never change, like the way the boys always close their performance with "Twist and Shout'. Now, they'd invited me back to their flat in Green Street and I hadn't really thought about how I was going to get there. I certainly wasn't prepared for them to play the final crashing chords of "Twist and Shout" and start to run off the stage almost before the curtains had closed.

"Come on, Al!" They grabbed me by the arms and hustled me along the corridors and passages until we reached the stage door, which opened as if by magic as we ran up to it. Outside was their Austin Princess limousine with the engine running and the doors already open. In front of the Princess was a police car with its blue light flashing and behind was a police motorcycle escort.

All this I saw in the second it took to be pushed bodily into the back seat of the Princess. Then near-disaster struck. Ringo's foot got stuck in the door of the car!

Everyone started yelling at him, "Pull your foot in, for God's sake, hurry up, what's the delay? Come on, Ring!" When I looked out through the front windscreen of the car I saw why they were all so worried.

The path from the stage door was being held open by a line of policemen with arms linked. Behind them was a solid mass of fans, all screaming and tearing at the line of police, trying to get through to lay their hands on the Beatles.

My God, the line was beginning to break! Now I too was shouting at Ringo, telling him to move his bloody foot. It can only have been seconds that we were delayed, but seconds seem like hours when you're in front of a bursting dam!

As soon as the rear doors were closed, we shot off past the crumbling police cordon, with a hail of love letters and God knows what pattering down on the bodywork of the car. When we turned the left-hand corner at the end of the road I looked back and saw that the brave line of police had at last been breached. There was a solid wall of humanity surging towards us. It was as terrifying as it must have been to stand in front of the starting stall at the Grand National — except that the horses at least are trained to jump!

We soon outdistanced the running mob, though if we'd had a puncture I wouldn't like to think what might have happened. Then there was a heady race through the centre of London, hammering through all the red lights, speeded on our way by policemen who were stationed at the big junctions just to stop the traffic in our favour. At last we reached the flat and I poured myself the largest and unsteadiest drink I can ever remember! If that was a sample of Beatlemania, what have I let myself in for? It's a terrifying thought that my new job is to take responsibility for their travel arrangements, but now that I've felt all the excitement of it I wouldn't be anywhere else in the world!

London

The Beatles were booked to play at one of the big cinemas in Manchester. They'd gone over earlier and were already in a state of siege at the cinema, but Brian and I had decided to stop in the centre of Manchester to have a bite to eat. We'd driven over from Liverpool in Brian's little maroon MG. Brian's one of the world's worst drivers by his own admission, so it didn't surprise me that he made a absolute hash of parking outside the restaurant. There we were, rowing backwards and forwards to try to park the MG in quite a big space. Backwards . . .thump. . .forwards . . .thump! Brian managed to hit both the car in front and the car behind, but no damage was done. There was a policeman on the other side of the street watching us with a broad grin on his face at Brian's antics. He could tell Brian wasn't drunk and incapable, just incapable!

After the meal, we came out to find that a heavy clinging fog had come down, a real pea-souper, and it didn't get any better as we drove towards the venue. We weren't at all sure that we were on the right road and we picked our way from street light to street light with great care, keeping on the look out for road signs. Suddenly a massive shape loomed out of the gloom in front of us — a mounted policeman, his cape over the rump of the horse. He signalled to us to stop, rode round to Brian's side of the car and leaned down to speak to us. "Sorry, sir. You can't come through this way. All the roads are closed."

"Why's that?" asked Brian.

"There's a concert by the Beatles tonight. It's absolute pandemonium down the road — you know what the fans are like. We're sealing off the area so that the traffic jams don't get any worse."

"Well in a way I'm glad to hear that," grinned Brian. "Here's my card. I'm Brian Epstein, the Beatles" manager."

"Oh, that's different," laughed the policeman. "You can go through, but go carefully. I should park a bit away from the cinema if I were you."

Brian shut the window and we drove cautiously on through two more police checkpoints until we arrived at the outer fringes of the crowd. There was no need to ask where the cinema was; we just had to follow the short skirts and Beatle haircuts!

Brian decided to take the policeman's advice and park half a mile from the cinema, which meant that we had to push and shove our way through the army of screaming fans that was laying siege to all the doors of the cinema. It must have looked strange — two respectably dressed businessmen pushing through a crowd of hysterical young girls! At last we reached the main door, where we showed our cards and were let in.

When we entered the foyer, it looked as though there had been a major disaster. Spread out on cots over most of the available floor space were sixty or seventy young girls, some still screaming, some moaning softly, but most totally unconscious! There were a few St. John's Ambulance volunteers rushing around, totally overwhelmed by the scale of the whole thing. We stepped delicately over the lines of bodies, like visitors to a casualty clearing station in a battle, and went on to face the next problem.

This came in the barrel-shaped and middle-aged guise of the cinema commissionaire. He's one of the officials paid to stand in front of the door to the dressing room and to let no one in — not a single Beatle fan and most certainly not a Beatle manager! The boys have a name for his type — "Mr. Jobsworthy".

Brian flashed his card at this imposing official, who hardly gave it a glance. Totally unimpressed, like a sergeant-major casting a despairing eye over the latest batch of raw recruits, this Mr Jobsworthy merely squared his shoulders and blew through his moustache.

"Good evening," said Brian politely. "I'm Brian Epstein, the manager of the Beatles. May we come through to the dressing room, please?"

"Sorry, sir. I've got orders to let absolutely no one through this door."

The man's moustache gave the self-satisfied twitch of a minor official who thinks he's on safe ground.

"But that's ridiculous," argued Brian. "I'm the manager of the Beatles.

"Sorry, sir. I don't care who you are, sir. It's more than my job's worth to let anyone through — even you."

At this I lost my temper totally. Thrusting Brian aside, I shoved my card under the commissionaire's moustache and snarled, "Look here, sunbeam, if you ever want to work again, move out of our bloody way!"

I think this persuaded him. Anyway, he let us through into the holy of holies.

It wasn't long before the Beatles were due on stage, so Brian and I had a quick word with them to check all was going well and then we took up our positions on the left in the wings. The screaming outside had been bad enough, but in the cinema it defied description. None of the supporting acts had a chance; their music was totally drowned by the incessant shrieking from two thousand throats. And if we thought that was the best the fans could manage, they proved us wrong when the boys finally took the stage.

Some noise is so intense that it makes you dizzy and I was reeling by the time the Beatles struck up the first number. I can't even recall what they played, even though all the amplifiers were turned up full. Everything they sang was battered down like snowdrops in a hurricane by the barrage of screaming. And I thought the Cavern was noisy!

Every so often John, Paul and George would turn their backs on the audience. At first I though this was to avoid the rain of jelly babies and toilet rolls inscribed with messages of undying love that were littering the stage. But no, I noticed that they weren't even singing, just miming from relaxed faces. As George moved towards the amplifiers near me for another session of knob-twiddling, I saw that they weren't even bothering to finger the chords, just hitting any old notes. When George came within a foot or two of where I was standing, I shouted, "What are you playing at?"

"Saving our voices," he yelled, and went off, grinning broadly.

This went on for about three numbers, while the boys took a well-deserved rest. I'm sure none of the fans suspected a thing, not even those near the front! At last they went back to singing and playing at full blast, trying to push back the opposing screaming. It didn't seem that we'd been there more than a few minutes before they struck up "Twist and Shout', the final song. A few notes must have penetrated to the crowd because the noise of screaming became even more horrendous as the climax approached.

As soon as they hit the last chords, the boys dropped their guitars on the stage. Ringo jumped down from his rostrum and they all ran for the door like Olympic sprinters trying to outrace a tidal wave. In a minute they were aboard their car and away down the road.

This time it wasn't my job to go with them, thank God. All Brian and I had to do was mop our brows, recover from the strange psychic excitement which a Beatles concert always generates and drive back to Liverpool. We were so deafened that we couldn't hear the engine of that sports car at all!

London

Well, here we are, installed at Sutherland House, the new London Headquarters of NEMS Enterprises. We've rented the whole fifth floor of this building and Brian's had it fitted out with the most modern half-partitioned offices and office furniture. It's all been done in Brian's usual style, with no expense spared, but instead of buying the equipment Brian has leased everything from a firm called Black Arrow Leasing. That's the smart way to avoid large tax bills, apparently.

I'm glad that the whole operation has at last moved to London. There were times when I thought we'd never leave Liverpool, Brian was so fussy about his choice of a London office. I've just realized that it's about five months since he appointed me General Manager. It seems like only yesterday that Brian was talking about me coming up to work in Liverpool — for just a month or so, supposedly. "We're in trouble in the Liverpool office. We need you there as soon as you can come," he said.

"Now hold it, Brian. We live in London now. Lesley and I have taken a super flat in Clapham South," I protested.

"I know that," he insisted. "We're moving the offices down here, starting with the Press Office. Why do you think I've got this new house we've been buying carpets for? All I'm asking is for you to come and sort out the Liverpool offices for a month or so. You can come down to London to see Lesley every Friday night and come back to Liverpool on Monday morning. I'll pay your expenses, don't worry."

It's been nearly five months of weekending between Liverpool and London for me and it hasn't been great fun. I gave up using the train very early because British Railways are electrifying the lines between London and Liverpool and that means suffering huge delays in the hope of an improved service in the years to come. Just my luck.

NEMS ENTERPRISES LTD

DIRECTORS: B. AND C. J. EPSTEIN

PRESS OFFICE : 13, MONMOUTH STREET, LONDON W.C.2. TELEPHONE COVent Gdn 2332

Monday 2 March 1964

CHANGE OF ADDRESS

This month Brian Epstein moves his company offices from Liverpool to London. With effect from the morning of

MONDAY 9 MARCH 1964

the new address for NEMS ENTERPRISES LTD and NEMS PRESENTATIONS LTD, previously located in Liverpool will be

SUTHERLAND HOUSE (5th FLOOR)
5/6 ARGYLL STREET
LONDON W.1.

The suite at Sutherland House will include the PRESS AND PUBLICITY DEPARTMENTS previously located in Monmouth Street.

For All Departments Please Telephone REGent 3261

J. ALISTAIR TAYLOR
General Manager
(Home telephone: KELvin 7345).

J. B. MONTGOMERY
Accounts.

TONY BARROW
Press and Public Relations Officer
(Home telepnone: REDpost 2735).

BRIAN SOMERVILLE
Beatles' Personal Press Representative
(Home telephone: STReatham 3987).

WENDY HANSON
Personal Assistant to Brian Epstein.

The following artists are under the sole direction of Brian Epstein:-

THE BEATLES ::: GERRY AND THE PACEMAKERS ::: BILLY J. KRAMER
THE DAKOTAS ::: CILLA BLACK ::: THE FOURMOST ::: TOMMY QUICKLY
SOUNDS INCORPORATED ::: THE REMO FOUR

With Compliments from

Tony Barrow

Press & Public Relations Officer

NEMS ENTERPRISES LTD

DIRECTORS: B AND C. J. EPSTEIN

SUTHERLAND HOUSE, 5/6 ARGYLL STREET, LONDON, W.1

TELEPHONE: REGENT 3261

Welcome to the new offices!

Attached is a copy of a letter which is being sent out to all artistes. I hope you will note its most important message: "that Nems Enterprises provides the finest and most efficient management/direction of artistes in the world". This must be without question our principal aim and should be borne in mind by all staff.

Alistair Taylor will be advising you of the details of operating the new offices, but I would like personally to point out one or two things.

First of all as our organisation is very much in the public eye, it is most important that we present the best possible "front". By this I mean that all visitors must be treated with utmost courtesy. That work must be carried out smoothly and efficiently without fuss. And most important, that the offices themselves must be kept tidy and clean at all times.

Another matter which I must ask you to treat with considerable care is the question of divulging to unauthorised or persons outside the organisation information concerning the company. It is strictly out of order for anyone to discuss with the press any business (however slight or remotely connected) whatsoever. Your adherence to this ruling is of great importance.

I really hope that you will be happy and as comfortable as possible in our new surroundings.

With best wishes for the future.

P.S. If there should be anything which you may wish to discuss with me, please do not hesitate to ask my assistant Eileen Lewis for an appointment - she will arrange it quickly. I would like you to know that the general welfare of personnel within the organisation is of the utmost importance to me.

Recently, I started to use the plane service to Heathrow, but what with all the driving to and from the airport, that takes just as long. Never mind, that's all over now. We're settled in and ready to hit London in a big way. Is London ready for us?

London

I had my hands on a vast sum of money this week, more than I ever imagined anyone could earn. Too bad that it didn't belong to me, but at least I looked after it for a while.

Brian likes me to be in the office at Sutherland House half an hour before anyone else arrives. This is so that I can open all the mail (except anything addressed privately to Brian) and check on the running of the business. It's not really spying, but Brian is a stickler for running the business correctly and he wants to know if we're receiving letters saying, "I have not received a reply to my letter of a fortnight ago..." If there's anything like that in the mail, Brian gives the person responsible for the delay a rocket. There's nothing he hates more than inefficiency.

Sometimes it's a real drag making it to the office that early, especially when I've been up till the small hours looking after one of our artistes. There have been times when I've said hello to the milkman as I came in!

Brian went off last Thursday night, telling me me that he "d be back on Monday. Would I look after the office while he was away? No problem, Brian.

I arrived at Sutherland House even earlier than usual and started to go through the mail. Most of it was fairly standard stuff, until I came to the last envelope, an ordinary-looking long white one. I ripped it open, and pulled out a compliments slip from EMI, with a check attached.

One look at the check was enough to turn me absolutely cold. It was made out to NEMS Enterprises to the value of over six million pounds! I fumbled for the compliments slip, which stated that the check was for three months" royalties from record sales. I just couldn't believe that a responsible company would send a check like that through the ordinary postal system, without even registering it! One tear in opening it would have meant a lot of embarrassment for me, but even more for EMI when Brian found out.

Keeping a tight grip on the check, I did a bit of mental arithmetic. Over six million pounds for three months means twenty-five million in a full year. And that's from record sales alone — excluding profits from music publishing, concert appearances, etc! It was a total surprise to me, as Brian keeps all financial details strictly to himself. No one here apart from Brian has any inkling of what really vast sums are being made — that's one of Brian's immovable principles. Its" one thing to see that the boys have sold a million or two of a single, another thing entirely to hold six million quid in your hand! I gave up trying to work out how many times my salary goes into twenty-five million.

Brian will go bananas, I thought, as I folded the check and put it into my pocket. Not only has this check come in an open letter, it could also have declared to the world the state of the Beatles" finances if it had come into the wrong hands. The problem was, what to do with it until Monday? I couldn't leave it in the office and I certainly didn't want to bank it until Brian had seen it, so I took it home for the weekend, checking my pocket every few seconds to make sure it hadn't crawled out.

Back home, I held out the envelope to Lesley and said, "Take that out of the envelope and hold it in your hand just for a minute. You're never likely to see anything like it again!"

First thing on Monday morning I went into Brian's office and showed him the flimsy envelope, the scruffy compliments slip and the huge check . Just as I expected, he did his nut. He took one look at them and lifted the phone at once. As soon as he was put through to Sir Joseph Lockwood, the Chairman of EMI, Brian started to tell him what he thought of EMI's business practices.

I thought I'd been hammered by Brian once or twice, but it was nothing compared to what Sir Joseph received. I crept out and left Brian to it. They'll probably send the next check round with a motorcycle escort!

But what a revelation! I never knew sums like that were involved. It's only two or three years ago that I was slipping two quid under the table in the Tower Ballroom to John so that he could stand his round of drinks (must get that back sometime)! Now we're talking about sums of money that are utterly astronomical. You could buy fifty thousand Minis with twenty-five million! What have we started — and where is it going to end?

London

I read once that when there was only one elephant in captivity in this country people who'd seen it used to say, "I've seen everything now. I've seen the elephant!" as if there were nothing more wonderful to behold on the surface of the earth. Well, now that I've recovered from Brian's latest party, I can truly say that I too have seen the elephant!

When Brian gives a party, everything is perfect, with nothing left to chance. It sounds quite ordinary, until you've seen the serried ranks of silverware on the snowy, immaculately laundered tablecloths, the exquisite flower arrangements, the quite unobtrusive attendants and waiters. Then you realize how scruffy your own parties have been.

A few weeks before the party, I heard a whisper that Brian was going to throw a spectacular party. Like a good General Manager, I went along and asked what I could do to help.

"Nothing, Alistair, thank you. Absolutely nothing," Brian smiled secretively. "I am doing this alone."

"Are you sure?" I protested.

"Completely. You've got to have nothing to do with it. I'm having a tent on the roof of William Mews. That's all I'm going to tell you, but it's going to be wonderful.

I wondered about this. Brian's flat is at the top of the building Whaddon House, and the roof is flat, so I supposed that he was going to have a rooftop party with dancing above Belgrave Square and a marquee at one end in case it rained or was cold. Still, I left it to him as he'd ordered, but I was fascinated by the stream of designers and decorators who suddenly were taking up so much of Brian's time.

At last the invitation landed on my desk. "Mr. Brian Epstein At Home on Wednesday August 12th at 15, Whaddon House, William Mews, London SW1, Buffet Supper..."

Off Lesley and I trundled in a taxi to the party, to be let in by Lonnie, Brian's tall black manservant. Lonnie took us to the foot of a ladder which led to the roof. Up we went and there we were confronted by Brian's tent. It spanned the entire roof! The whole of the flat area was covered in the most incredible pink and white striped canopy with windows in it overlooking London and columns of white and pink carnations every few yards. Dotted about on all sides of the small dance floor were clusters of gilded chairs around gilded tables. The food was in a kind of alcove and not even a Roman emperor could have put on such a display. There was an enormous bowl of caviar, the posterity of a shoal of sturgeon, and all through that long night it was refilled so that it never seemed to diminish. For Brian to have any of his guests feel that the food and drink might have finite limits would have been impossible. The champagne just flowed and flowed, but if the guests were drunk it wasn't the fine wines, but the sheer magnificence of the scene that worked on them.

That ladder ought to be taken and put in a museum of show business, if anyone ever opens one in this country. The feet that went up and down it belonged to all the most famous personalities who are in the country at the moment. There were not just today's new stars, but legendary names like Judy Garland. The Beatles were all there, of course, and they've compiled a huge tape of their own music and other NEMS artistes" music to keep us entertained the whole night through. It was all magic, but the memory I shall always treasure is seeing Brian's parents, Harry and Queenie, with expressions on their faces of pure pride in their son's achievements, as they watched him surrounded by his stars and the other glittering guests.

The police kept appearing, of course. Once it was past midnight and the music was still belting out over Belgravia, some of the neighbors started ringing up the local station and complaining. Every so often, a uniformed bobby would appear at the top of the ladder, look around as if to say, "Cor, look who's here!"; and slip down out of sight. At one point, I thought I'd better oil the wheels of justice, and I slipped one of the policemen a bottle of champagne.

"Here, take this back to the station and have a drink on us."

"Thanks," the policeman grinned. He turned to his mate. "I can't hear any noise, can you?" he shouted above the thundering music!

Eventually, at about half-past three, Lesley and I left with Tony Barrow and his wife in their Mini. When we'd gone a fair way, Tony stopped the car and we looked back. All we could see was this pink tent suspended in the night sky like a giant balloon over Belgravia and all we could hear, even half a mile away, was the music of the Beatles hammering away over London. A long, long way from a plate of shellfish in the Basnett Bar!

Paul's Scottish home, High Park, in Argyll. (Alistair Taylor)

4
CHAPTER

London

The boys" concert at the Prince of Wales Theatre the other night was one of their best shows, probably because they were so relaxed.

It's one of our best venues. We've been leasing it off Delfont recently for Sunday evening concerts, and you'll find us presenting not only NEMS talent there, but also people like Georgie Fame. But without doubt the Beatles" night was our biggest thrill — and our biggest worry.

The problem for me is that the stage door in the Prince of Wales is just about as public as it could be. It's not up some dingy little alleyway, like most theatres we use. Oh no, it opens right out into a busy street and anybody going in or out is about as conspicuous as a refugee climbing over the Berlin Wall. It was definitely designed before the days of Beatlemania!

This produced one of my worst headaches when I first surveyed the entrances and exits of the theatre. There was no way the boys could just drive up to either the front door or the stage door and hope to get through in one piece. Nor are there any convenient little side doors, lavatory windows or handy cat flaps to sneak in through! The only openings at the back are two exits for the audience, the kind where an attendant pushes a bar from inside and the door opens outwards — not a lot of use when you want to come in, since there isn't a handle on the outside. And you can't land a helicopter on the roof (the thought has crossed my mind more than once). This was definitely a job for Mr. Fixit, as the boys call me.

A few days before the concert, I "cased the joint', wandering all round the building, weighing up all the limited options —all two of them: go in through the front door or through the stage door. Then it was back to the office, a few cups of strong coffee and a session with the thinking cap on. As usual, there was only one really feasible answer, and that turned out, as so often, to be the simplest.

Came the evening of the concert, came the police in ranks several helmets deep, came the fans in their madding thousands. If we'd come in by helicopter, we'd have seen what appeared to be a sea of people breaking in waves against the walls of the theatre, with the occasional blue breakwater formed by the lines of police with arms linked. If the architects of the theatre could have seen it, they'd have bitten their pencils in two; the building wasn't meant to be besieged!

At the front entrance there were metal barriers holding the mobs back and keeping the road open a little, but we don't rely on them too much. You should see how bent they can be at the end of the evening. It wasn't much better at the back, where another screaming, baying mob was surrounding the stage door., Not a flea could have crawled in unnoticed, never mind a Beatle!

Standing outside one of the two outward-opening exit doors was a young man in his twenties, too old to be a serious fan, nonchalantly holding a briefcase in one hand and a cigarette in the other. The fans weren't mobbing that door, and the police weren't taking too much notice of the young man either . . . but they knew something the fans didn't.

Arrival time. Around the corner came the usual black-windowed limousine, unmistakably the Beatles" transport. You could have heard the cheering and screaming a mile away as the fans surged forward against the thin blue line of police. Some helmets rolled into the road, but the line held firm. Straight up the street swept the darkened car, to turn right at the top into the main street and head for the front door of the theatre. The Beatles are arriving at the front door! Come on, everyone. It's no good waiting here, let's dash round to the front.

This time the police offered curiously little resistance to the crowd as it broke through their line and raced off in pursuit of the car. The young man by the exit door threw down his cigarette into the discarded piles of Beatle placards and ground it out under his heel.

A few seconds later, round the same corner swept a plain and ordinary Jaguar. As it reached the door where the young man stood, it slammed to a stop. The young man kicked twice with his heel on the door and stepped smartly aside as it was pushed open by the attendant waiting inside. At the same moment, the doors of the Jaguar opened and John, Paul, George and Ringo emerged, totally unruffled and undisturbed. They calmly walked through the exit door into the theatre and the attendant slammed the door shut. Mission accomplished. Four relaxed and happy Beatles delivered, ready to start their night's work.

By this time, the young man with the briefcase was strolling off in the opposite direction from the riot going on at the front door. A few of the fans who'd been tricked into chasing an empty car would have liked to talk to him, no doubt! The few fans who'd been left behind in the rush to the front were still recovering from the shock of seeing the Beatles arrive at a theatre as calmly as Auntie Mabel coming home with the shopping; they paid the young man no attention.

Three guesses who the young man with the cigarette was.

Glasgow

Here I am with another few minutes to spare from the usual rush and push. I'm just settling accounts with the people here at the hotel and watching the crowds begin to break up and go home.

Staying in the middle of cities like this usually causes big problems. It's not the way we behave. I've never had any complaints about the behavior of the Beatles or any of our acts and no hotel has ever refused to have us back. No, the problem is the fans.

It never takes them long to realize where we're staying and then we're under siege until we move on. How do they know? Do they tap our telephone lines? Do we have a traitor in the office? Still, if we book into a hotel out of town, we can always vary our route to and from the concerts and not so many fans actually have the transport to get out to us. Staying in town like we did last night means a much tighter and riskier arrangement for transport.

We really did the fans this morning, though. I looked out of the window of my hotel as soon as I woke up and there must have been a thousand or more of them waiting outside. The front door of the hotel seemed a suicidal exit. We'd have been torn to pieces. These aren't quiet autograph hunters politely offering you their books to sign. They're hysterical fanatics with all the enthusiasm of a tribe of cannibals chasing a wounded missionary. We simply daren't ever be caught in the open. These crowds are like huge animals; they can kill you with love just by rolling over you.

Now, like James Bond, I always have an escape route planned. This time it was the luggage lift! Very considerately, this goes down from the hotel to the main concourse of the railway station, so I told our driver to wait on the platform of the station, with his engine running.

All the time we were eating breakfast, the boys looked jumpy; they weren't eating much. This wasn't exactly surprising, as the crowds were getting bigger and noisier by the minute and none of them relished the thought of going out of the front door.

"Al, how are we going to get out of here?"

"Can you get us out of here in one piece?"

"Sure." I said, calmly finishing my coffee. "No problem."

When the time came to leave, everyone was standing in the reception hall looking faint and pale, like settlers besieged in their lonely farmhouse by hostile redskins. All it needed was a fire arrow to come whizzing through the window! Outside, the police were manning the barricades, with difficulty. Like Tarzan, I simply said, "Follow me," and led them round to the back of the hotel and into the great Victorian luggage lift.

"Right, when the lift doors open, run for the car. It'll be in front of you. Going down."

The attendant took us down smoothly. Just before we reached the station concourse, I had a vision of what might be waiting for us if things had gone wrong and the fans had realized that we were coming out this way: hundreds of girls screaming and trying to reach us through the concertina barrier of the lift, like something out of a horror movie. But no, all was quiet. There were only respectable commuters and railway porters to be seen.

"Go for it!" I yelled, and we charged across the concourse to the car, leapt in head first on top of each other and told the driver to take us away. As we roared through the entrance of the station, I saw people mouthing to each other: "That's the Beatles." It was! By the time the cannibals realized that the missionaries had escaped from the cooking pot, we were miles away! Today's score: Fans 0 Beatles 1.

London

It's one of my main jobs to make sure that the boys can move about safely.

What about the police? Where were they while all this frantic escaping in luggage lifts was going on? Well, in fact I had to get their permission to change the arrangements and they held back the crowds at the front of the hotel while we escaped by means of the luggage lift.

I think our police are wonderful (someone's already said that, haven't they?). Getting the boys into and out of theatres is like a smash and grab raid in reverse. The police and I have to cooperate in working out a split-second timetable, checking all the likely trouble spots and trying to avoid problems before they arise. This often means hours of map-reading and driving over the routes beforehand so that as far as possible we know what we'll be facing. Then the plan has to be approved by the boys, who, after all, have to arrive at their gigs fresh and able to play straight away. It'd be no good them getting travel-sick or accidentally trapping their hands in a car door. That's the stuff of my nightmares!

Of course, all our plans are different from each other, because every venue throws up different problems. One thing never changes, though. It's truly incredible how the grapevine spreads the news to the fans so that at times it seems as if they know what we're going to do even before we decide to do it! Sometimes we use decoy cars, changing from our limousine to a shabby van in some convenient lay-by outside town. Then the limousine goes to the stage door of the theatre to be mobbed by screaming fans and get "I love George" scrawled over it in lipstick. Meanwhile a battered old van chugs slowly round to the side entrance (usually next to the dustbins). The theatre door will be unlocked from the inside, the back doors of the van will open on well-oiled hinges, the local pigeons will catch a brief glimpse of John, Paul, George, Ringo and Alistair rushing through into the theatre and then the door will slam shut. Operation completed, the fans are frustrated by the empty limousine, the boys appear on stage on time and spic and span.The fans think, "Is there an underground passage into this place that we missed?"

Coming out of a theatre can be even more difficult, because the fans are ready for us. Take yesterday, for instance. The boys had to leave a theatre down a very long and narrow alleyway running off the main road, just like the sort of ravine where the wagon train is ambushed by the Indians in a Western. When we tried to leave, the fans were going to head us off at the pass, without a doubt! After casting around for a bit and talking to the local police, I came up with this one.

Halfway through the performance, I arranged for a van to reverse down the alley to the stage door. The fans, being held back by the straining line of police, knew who was going to be going off in that! We opened the rear doors of the van so that they were right up against the stage door and waited for the final chords of "Twist and Shout', always the cue for even more screaming as the fans realize that the concert is ending.

Less than a minute after the music died away, the fans could see what they were after. In the gap under the open doors of the van, four pairs of legs appeared and dived into the back of the darkened van. An attendant (guess who) slammed the doors shut and the driver accelerated away down the narrow space that the police were holding open and on to the open road. Some of the fans went charging off after the van, hoping that it might be caught at the traffic lights, others went off home happy to say they'd seen at least the legs of John, Paul, George and Ringo!

Anyone on the other side of the theatre would have seen a little public access door open a few minutes later. Four Beatles strolled out into the darkened and peaceful street and climbed leisurely into the back of the other vehicle that had been waiting for them round the corner, which zoomed away. The four pairs of legs that the fans had seen belonged to four stage hands who'd had a bit of exercise diving into the van and being taken for a nice little ride round the block.

This isn't to say that there's never a hitch in the arrangements. Only last week we had a repeat performance of a very familiar old hiccup-and it was all down to the police! I'd arranged for our car to be met at the usual deserted lay-by outside town by an unmarked police van. Everything seemed to be going perfectly: the lay-by contained only the police van and there were no bystanders or hordes of pursuing fans.

The boys quickly got out of their limousine, said a quick hello to the driver, and we all climbed into the back of the van. Off we went, in the expert care of the police driver, who was dressed like a plumber's mate.

This is for me the moment when the adrenaline starts to pump round my veins, the moment when things are really out of my control and I just have to trust that everyone has followed their instructions to the letter. I keep looking at my watch, working out where we are and trying to judge from the noise when we arrive how many fans are outside and how far away they are. Not easy to work out, in an enclosed van!

This time, we seemed to be driving very quickly, more quickly than we needed to arrive at the theatre on time. Perhaps there was a traffic jam ahead or a diversion which would mean a long detour from the arranged route. Suddenly we slowed down, bounced over a curb and screeched to a standstill.

"OK lads, this must be it," I said. "When I give the word, open the doors and go straight in through the little red door. Mal will be there to lead you to your dressing room." That's Big Mal Evans the roadie. "Right ! Now! Go for it!"

The doors banged open as John leaned on them and we all fell out of the van. But wait! There isn't a red door, there isn't even a theatre! There's a row of police cars, Z-cars, and moving towards us a crowd of policemen and civilians. Hang on, I know this place; it's the yard of the local police station. We've been kidnapped — again!

John just turned around and said to the nearest copper, "Do we get time off for good behavior if we confess now and promise to do a Christmas show in the local nick?"

The crowd had reached us now, PCs, sergeants, traffic wardens, brass hats, detectives, tea-ladies, all with their families, all clutching records and autograph books for the boys to sign. There must have been half the local force there. If only the local villains had known what a chance they had to so some uninterrupted thieving!

There we were, madly signing and shaking hands, me with an anxious eye on the clock. Five minutes later, we piled back into the van and the "plumber's mate" took us to the theatre dead on time. No plumber's van ever went so fast.

So if ever a policeman offers you a Beatles autograph, you can rely on it being genuine, even if it does look hastily scrawled!

London

Did you see the crowds on television today? It must have been the biggest ever turn-out of fans at Heathrow — something like ten or twelve thousand screaming teenagers. Well, it's not every day that the boys come back from a tour!

I had been helping to plan the arrangements of their return for weeks before they even departed. The chaos at the airport is getting so bad every time the Beatles fly in or out that the police and airport authorities keep asking us not to have the boys using Heathrow during the school holidays. They're afraid that one day the fans will block the tunnel that leads into the centre of Heathrow and bring Britain's major international airport to a complete standstill! It's very nearly happened a few times but we've always managed to keep the fans on the move. Anyway, they don't want to stand in a drafty tunnel waiting to see the Beatles; they want to be on the roof of the Queen's Building already screaming as the boys" plane taxies on to the apron. Then they can let out an enormous supercharged scream as the door of the plane swings open and the fab four step out on to the stairs. As for the idea of having the Beatles travelling only in the school term-time, anyone who thinks it would make any difference to the size of the crowds must be living in Cloud Cuckoo Land! The fans would only play truant from school; there'd be a massive epidemic of twenty-four hour flu!

This time the arrangements for meeting the boys were rather different from usual. Each Beatle was assigned one of us to look after him at the airport and see him safely home. My special responsibility was taking care of John and Cynthia, who's been with John on this tour. The aim was to finish the press conference as quickly as possible, then pile into the cars, and split up in four different directions in order to try to shake off the pursuing fans.

It was too bad that the press conference went on for far too long. Why we have to have the boys asked a lot of meaningless questions the minute they step off a plan defeats me; I suppose it's all good publicity, but sometimes it can be too dearly bought. By the time we came out into the open, the fans had broken out from the roof of the Queen's Building and were pushing the thin blue line of the police cordon back towards the cluster of parked cars. The mob was like a giant animal, screaming from one red throat. I could see twelve-foot metal barriers buckling like drinking straws under the pressure of bodies and that's not a funny sight when you're on the other side! Can 15-year-old girls really be doing this?

The boys have been all over the world, but I don't think they've seen anything to match this. Their faces were white as we ran for the cars, dodging a hail of jelly babies and trying to avoid the policemen's helmets which were rolling on the ground.

John, Cynthia and I dived into the back of the faithful old Austin Princess, my favorite getaway car. John was shaking with fear and I don't blame him. He'd have been torn in pieces if he'd fallen into the clutches of that adoring mob.

"Get us out of here! Let's drive!" John kept shouting. The driver gunned the engine and we moved towards the tiny gap in the pandemonium that the police were struggling to keep open for us, like sailors in the Antarctic trying to go along a lead in the deadly pack-ice to the open sea.

There was no chance of using the main tunnel out of Heathrow. We were routed along the perimeter road alongside the runway. Like a comet trailing a tail of fire, we were followed by a hoard of fans, some on foot, some on cycles, scooters and motorbikes. We seemed to have attracted the biggest tail of any of the getaway cars, possibly because the Princess stands out as a famous Beatle car.

"Put your foot down and lose them!" I ordered the driver, and we accelerated faster than I thought a limousine could. When we turned on to the main road outside the airport and entered the heavy traffic, most of the fans dropped behind and were soon lost to view.

"Thank God for that," sighed John, as he settled back in his seat for a relaxing ride back to Weybridge. I stretched out too, sure that we'd pulled off another escape and that there would be nothing more to bother us.

I thought too soon. The driver turned to us and said, "There's a motorcyclist behind who's been following us for the last five miles. I think he was at the airport, too."

I looked around and, sure enough, there was a motorcyclist keeping station on us, dressed in black leathers and helmet. This looked a very sinister figure, especially the way he was just following, not even trying to draw level.

"Shake him off!" I ordered, and the Princess fairly picked up her skirts and ran. Behind, the motorcyclist twisted his throttle and closed the gap. Our driver put the car through a slalom of violent manoeuvres, tracking from lane to lane and making all sorts of unexpected turns. The only result was that we all felt sick. We were coming nearer and nearer to Weybridge and the motorcyclist was coming nearer and nearer to us.

Suddenly John spoke up, "Oh, stop the car and we'll see what the feller wants."

Before I could work out whether this was going to be a good idea or not, the car had come to a halt and John was already opening the door and beckoning to the motorcyclist, who had stopped a few yards behind us. "Come on, mate," he said. "Now why are you following us? Hop in and let's have a chat."

The stranger put his bike on its stand, took off his helmet and stepped into the car, with a look of wonder on his face as if it had been Captain Nemo's submarine. John pulled down the occasional seat which faced the rear seats and asked him to sit down. Then, by the side of the road, with all the traffic pounding by mere inches away, the two of them chatted like good mates for five or ten minutes about records, the tour, the bike, all sorts of things.

At last, John signed his autograph on a piece of paper for the stranger, opened the door and said, "Cheerio, mate. Go steady now." The motorcyclist waved his black gauntlet and went off in the opposite direction with his day, no, his year made! He'd probably thought John was going to thump him! Now, what wouldn't a journalist have given for five minutes" chat with John Lennon in the back of the Beatles" car?

It was an absolutely natural and generous thing for John to do, especially when he was jet-lagged and still in a state of shock from the scene at the airport. All the same, it was a risk I'd rather he hadn't taken. It's my job to protect him but I can't do that if he invites total strangers into the car like that. I think he was lucky that this time the stranger only wanted to have a chat. Nine hundred and ninety nine thousand, nine hundred and ninety-nine Beatle fans out of a million might be as gentle as lambs if met on their own. But there's always the millionth chance. John should go steady, now.

London

A bit of information has just landed on my desk about the boys" return to Heathrow — the bill! We've had a number of claims direct to us and some through the airport authorities and it seems that nine cars were totally flattened by the army of fans! I've just been out to have a look at them and they look as if a steam-roller has gone right over them. The bonnets and boots are caved in and the roofs have been bent flush to the steering wheels. Another bill for the insurers to argue about, I expect, but I'm sure it will be settled quickly. It would be bad publicity if we didn't do something.

These fans are amazing. They treat the whole thing like some gigantic battle of wits, with the police as the opponents, and the Beatles as the jackpot prize. There's no malice in them, at least. I've not heard of any policeman being seriously hurt on Beatles crowd control duty and none of the fans seem to go in for assaulting the police. It's more like a huge pushing contest and you can often see some of the policemen grinning as they link arms and lean back against the crowd. One or two have even told me that Beatles duty is a prized job at their stations, almost as desirable as sunning themselves watching the cricket at a Test Match! Whatever turns you on, I suppose, but I wouldn't fancy being any nearer those frenzied girls than I have to be.

Property seems to be fair game with the fans. Like I said, I've seen huge metal crash barriers bent into fantastic shapes just by the pressure of bodies. They can't feel any pain in the state they work themselves into. If you'd seen those cars today, you too would wonder what we've started here. I know teenage girls used to chase Frank Sinatra, and then Elvis Presley, but Beatlemania is beginning to look more and more like a form of madness. Even the psychologists the newspapers interview about it are at a loss to explain it, so I won't even try. Sometimes I have to pinch myself to try to remember that it was just three years or so ago that Brian and I were sitting in the Tower Ballroom watching the Beatles play, like any other band of local lads, and wondering what we could offer them!

The boys themselves are sometimes horrified at the scenes they have to fight their way through or escape from. None of us dares to think what would happen if the crowd ever laid hands on one of them. I just don't think he'd come out alive and in one piece. Great love, like great hate, just makes the fans completely without any thought of what they're doing. They'd wake up with a bit of Paul's jacket or

John's hair in their hands and wonder where it had come from! I only hope that no one's ever killed at one of these riots, fantastic as they are for all of us. The Beatles would surely get the blame, whatever the circumstances!

London

Roy Orbison is a really hospitable guy. The Beatles toured with him in the early days and they got on just fine. He's on tour over here just now and the other day the boys and I were invited to his birthday party held in the basement of a restaurant called Quo Vadis, in Soho. "Quo vadis" is Latin for "where are you going'. I didn't know that until the manager explained it to me at three o'clock in the morning.

Anyway, on the evening of the party, I sent for the limousine, collected the boys, and off we went. When we turned into the street where the restaurant is, there they were, dozens of fans, some carrying Beatles banners, and all waiting to fall on us! I told the driver to take the first side turning so that we would have to risk getting bogged down in the crowd, or, even worse, knocking one of the fans over. The boys didn't fancy the idea of going to the party at all and there were mutters of "let's get out of here'. But I wasn't going to miss a good party, even if they wanted to!

Telling the boys to draw the blinds of the limousine and drive away for about ten minutes, I slipped out of the car and made my way through the crowds into the restaurant. This is where being unknown can be really useful, because nobody made any attempt to connect me with the Beatles. I threaded my way round the tables, went down into the basement and said a quick hello to Roy. Then I made a beeline for the manager and explained the situation to him.

He led me to the rear of the basement, pushed open a fire door and revealed an alleyway almost blocked by the restaurant's huge dustbins! You could just see round the bins enough to make sure that the fans hadn't yet discovered this alley. Just the job, I thought.

I asked the manager to keep the door open and to expect us in a few minutes. Off I went back through the crowds and to the rendezvous with the boys in the limousine.

Sure enough, along came the car; I jumped in and told the boys what we had to do to get into the party. They had to crouch on the floor of the car and be ready to hurl themselves out as soon as we reached the entrance to the alleyway, then avoid the odd bits of banana skin and potato peeling and spring for the back door of Quo Vadis.

"Ta very much, Alistair. We never had to go to this much trouble when we gate-crashed parties at home. Now we're invited to a party and we need to go in like commandos!"

"Yeah, I wouldn't have bothered to wash if I'd known it wasn't a posh do."

We cruised down that dimly-lit back street, with me leaning over the driver's shoulder giving him precise instructions where to stop. Just as we were slowing down, some of the fans came round the corner (are they mind-readers?) and started making for us. That was it. Jam on the brakes, fling open the door and roll out down the alley, lads. Meanwhile I took my time over elegantly stepping out of the limousine — on the other side.

This totally threw the crowd. Some of them wanted to come on anyway, but others must have thought that I really was an eccentric millionaire who liked cruising down back streets and stopping to inspect pig bins. I tried to look conspicuous and snooty, while on the other side of the car the Beatles were crawling on hands and knees through last week's cabbage leaves. They didn't even dare to attract attention to themselves by running, the fans were so close.

As the fans dispersed in disappointed little groups, furling their banners and muttering, I got into the limousine and asked the driver to take me round to the front door of Quo Vadis. After all, one has to arrive in style. When I reached the basement, everybody was roaring with laughter at the boys, who were wiping unmentionable muck off their elbows and knees! I've heard of gate-crashing but never of bin-crashing!

London

In the time since I've been back with the boys, I've seen Brian under more and more pressure. I think it's very easy to forget that only a couple of years have passed since he was just another hopeful manager hard-selling his group around London. In that time, he's become pop music's most famous businessman, most eligible bachelor of the year and all that sort of thing, and the positions are reversed. Half the world is now flocking to Brian's doorstep and I don't think that he always finds it pleasant. He's a very private man, moody and out-going by turns and sometimes quite unpredictable.

Last night Lesley and I were sitting quietly at home when the phone rang. Brian's voice was on the other end, sounding terribly strained:

"Hello, Alistair. I just want to tell you that it's all too much and I've had enough."

"Brian!" I gasped, feeling sandbagged. "Come on, you can't mean it! Tell me you're not serious!"

"No, sorry, my mind's made up. Thank you for everything. Goodbye, Alistair." Click.

I dialled for a car without pausing and as soon as it came told the driver to get me from Clapham South to William Mews in record time. What the hell could have brought Brian to this? He'd seemed so normal just a few hours previously — oh yes, under the usual pressure of work, but not suicidal.

All the lights were on as the car screeched to a halt outside Brian's home. As I told the driver to wait, another car drew up behind and out fell Vivienne Moynihan, one of our producers. I didn't even wait to ask her if she'd had the same phone call as me. I could see that she was just as agitated.

I leaned on Brian's doorbell, ringing continuously in the hope of waking him up if he was just slipping into unconsciousness. Surely that's what would happen, I thought. Nothing messy like a knife and nothing dangerous to other people like gas. God, the thoughts that can race through your head in ten seconds!

There was a sound from inside and the door opened. Brian was standing there in a dressing gown, immaculate as usual and looking completely calm and cool.

"What's wrong with you?" he asked, as if we were the ones in trouble.

"I thought you were about to ... well, what you said on the phone..." I answered lamely.

"Nonsense, I'm perfectly all right, as you can see. Now, go home and stop worrying about me. Really, Alistair, I shall be fine."

So we left, wondering whether we should have pressed Brian further. But he did look well in control of himself, and in the office this morning he was as normal as ever. All the same, I wonder about what's going on inside his head and I shan't sleep easy for a few nights, in case the phone rings again.

5

CHAPTER

London

The Beatles have been awarded MBE's!. We've all known for some time, of course, but we were sworn to secrecy until the Honours List was published. Everybody here is going around smiling as if it was Christmas.

Four musicians from Liverpool have made it to the top of the ladder — and put in a few extra rungs on the way! We always knew that the Beatles were loved by most people under the age of eighteen, but what's rocked us most is the way that trendy London society's taken up the boys. A party just isn't a party, my dear, unless there's at least one Beatle there! But an award like this was a bolt from the blue to me. I know the boys went down marvelously well at the Royal Variety Performance, not only with the Queen Mother, but also with the established stars like Marlene Dietrich, but we never expected an invitation to Buckingham Palace. Pop musicians just don't get that sort of treatment!

It's an honor for all Liverpool. I'm sure Liverpool will arrange a royal welcome home for the Beatles.

The London end of the arrangements has been my scene. Brian gave me a call the evening we heard about the awards, and he asked me to come over to his house. When I arrived, he was alone and quite subdued. We had a drink, then Brian turned to me and said quietly, "Alistair, we have to make sure that the Beatles get into and out of Buckingham Palace safely on the day of the ceremony. We can't have any mistakes or incidents which might embarrass the Queen. Will you liaise with the Palace and make sure that all the arrangements are absolutely watertight?

Wow! Alistair Taylor, one-time timber importer's clerk, now liaison officer for NEMS Enterprises to Buckingham Palace! If ever a fixit had to be done properly this one did!

I phoned the head of the Buckingham Palace constabulary —I never knew before that the Palace had its own independent force. He asked me to come down and have a meeting to discuss the security precautions. Well, I didn't imagine I'd ever penetrate the inside of the Palace again, so I decided to make the most of it. Close shave, best suit, rolled umbrella, mustn't let the Beatles down. Then into the car: "Buckingham Palace, please" I liked that bit almost the best!

The head of the Palace force doesn't fit the usual beetle-crusher (sorry) pattern. For a start, he wears civilian clothes and he's more like a senior diplomat than a copper. Underneath the urbane and charming manner is a very efficient professional. The essence of his job is foreseeing what might happen and making sure it doesn't Any incident or arrest at a Royal function would be a defeat for his force.

We worked together excellently. For once I was dealing with someone who understands what it's like to have to protect an immensely popular person. The Queen and the Beatles must, after all, be the most likely people to draw a crowd anywhere in this country. It's a good job they don't appear on the same bill very often!

Although I'm fairly new to the business of minding famous people, the policeman never once talked down to me. We discussed all the points of security and laid our very careful plans. When we'd finished our talks, we walked across the outer forecourt. The guardsman on duty came to a crashing salute as we walked past him! I know it was for the policeman and not for me, but to be saluted is still a thrill after spending two years in the RAF as the lowest form of National Serviceman! On our tour, I even had a peep at the inner courtyard, as close as I'm ever likely to come to royalty.

London

It worked, just as we planned! The Beatles have their MBEs and no one has been hurt and no one has caused any Royal embarrassment. Big sighs of relief all round.

The policeman at the Palace told me that on Investiture days it is the custom for those about to be honored to queue in their cars along the Mall, slowly filtering into the Palace forecourt. Well, that was out, for a start. Imagine the scenes if the Beatles were stuck in that sort of traffic jam for fifteen minutes. Perhaps they'd have got through in an armored car, but it would have looked a bit conspicuous among all the Rolls-Royces!

Eventually we came up with the answer you saw on the television. As you look at the Palace from the front, there are two main gates and a smaller one to the left. We agreed that the boys would come straight down the Mall, with a little help from the Metropolitan Police, and enter the forecourt through that gate, without a pause. That gate would then be slammed shut — fast!

And so it happened. The only trouble was outside, where the police had to keep hauling hysterical girls off the Palace railings! I don't know what the boys got up to in the Palace, but I'm sure Brian is very proud of them.

London

What a day! Sometimes this job pitchforks me from peace and quiet into major panics at a moment's notice. There I was in the office at Sutherland House this morning, working away quietly at general paperwork, when the telephone range. Goodbye to the humdrum dictating and signing; this was another crisis.

Brian was in a total panic. Did I know that John and Paul were due to collect an Ivor Novello award at the Savoy Hotel at lunchtime? Yes, of course I did. So what? The only snag was that Brian had forgotten to tell them the date, time or place! They were due to be at the Savoy at twelve-thirty for the formal presentation. I stole a glance at my watch. Eleven o'clock. "They'll never make it, Brian."

That sort of negative thinking never goes down well with Brian. The boys simply had to make it; for the Beatles to snub the music and entertainment establishment would be unthinkable. All that carefully cultivated image would be ruined just as surely as if we gave them crew-cuts. Oh, and there was one other small thing. Brian couldn't face telling John and Paul that he'd forgotten to tell them the arrangements. Would I invent some sort of cover story, please?

This meant that I really would have to take the blame and pretend that I'd forgotten to tell them. Of course, if this had been true, I'd have been sacked on the spot, but I had to hope that John and Paul would be in too much of a hurry to bother to work that out.

I knew that John was out at Weybridge, so I thought that I ought to contact him first, as he would have further to travel. I took a deep breath and dialled his number. If ever a story sounded lame, it was my attempt to apologize for something I hadn't done. I don't think I can put into writing what John said when he realized that I was seriously expecting him to drop everything and come up to London within two hours. I don't think the musical and entertainment establishment would be very pleased to hear his opinions. Mind you, I don't blame him. To be dragged out of bed and told that you're expected in front of the cameras at lunchtime must be fairly traumatic.

That left only Paul. I knew Paul wouldn't let me down, would he? Again, there was one tiny problem. Paul is staying at Jane Asher's family house in Wimple Street and I knew he had been out late last night. Would he be awake?

Sometimes every number I dial adds to the odds on my eventual heart attack. The tension was unbearable; the ringing tone seemed to go on forever. Surely no house can be that big that it takes this long to come to the phone? There can't be anyone in! Oh, please let him be in, and awake, and in a reasonable frame of mind.

At last the receiver was lifted by Mrs. Asher, Jane's mother. She is a lovely lady, and very protective of Paul and Jane. She couldn't possibly wake Paul this early, whatever the circumstances, not even for a crisis of this size. So I had reluctantly to agree to wait a while and ring back later to see if Paul had surfaced. All this time, the minutes were ticking away; the first guests must be already arriving at the Savoy, full of anticipation at seeing the Beatles receive their award. And there was going to be a great empty silence and two empty chairs.

I waited until nearly twelve o'clock, sitting on my hands and pacing about the office, if it's possible to do both of those things at the same time! This time I insisted that Mrs. Asher should go and wake Paul and very unwillingly she agreed. A few minutes later, a very sleepy and none-too-pleased Paul came on the line. In my best lame diplomatic style I told him the story I had been practicing for the last hour. There was a very long silence at the other end, until I thought he must have put the phone down. Then came the answer: "OK, be round in a cab to pick me up in ten minutes" time."

Good old Paul! Telling my secretary that I'd be back in about half-an-hour, I raced off to the taxi-rank and arrived at Wimple Street in about a quarter of an hour. As I dashed up to the top step, the door opened and there was Paul, immaculately washed, shaved and groomed, in a freshly pressed suit and clutching in his hand a piece of toast! His expression seemed to say, "What's the panic? Do I ever let you down?" And I knew that he'd been asleep not twenty minutes before!

The lunchtime rush hour was now in full spate, of course, and we took until twelve forty-five to make it to the Savoy. Everyone there was going berserk, wondering whether the Beatles were snubbing the ceremony. As we alighted from the taxi, crowds of reporters surged around us, scribbling, clicking and yelling questions. I was so hepped-up that I forced my way through without difficulty and led Paul into the foyer and through the entrance of the banqueting room.

There I turned to make my farewells, saying that I'd pick Paul up later on. But he wasn't having any of that. If I didn't come in with him, he wasn't going in either. "OK, Paul, I'll grab a seat somewhere along the side and watch." But that wasn't good enough. Paul absolutely insisted that I should come up to the top table and sit with him, or it was a nice deal! He'd go home straight away. Ivor Novello, or no Ivor Novello.

Now you must have seen a Variety Club lunch or dinner on television. The place was a Milky Way of stars; the diamonds and gold filled the room with glitter through the coiling wreaths of expensive cigar smoke. At every step on my knee-shaking way to the top table, there seemed to be someone whose face I recognized. I'm not easily overawed, but there was nowhere else I would rather have been at that moment. There I was, a professional anonymous nobody in a working suit, making my way to the summit of the showbiz mountain!

The top table stretched the width of the room, floodlit for the TV cameras. It was filled with big names; Billy Butlin, holiday camp magnate, David Frost, broadcaster extraordinary, Paul McCartney, surely the world's most successful songwriter, and Alistair Taylor . . . Who? I could hear the buzz going round the room. "Where's John? Who on earth is that with Paul?" I never felt so conspicuous in my life, but everyone at the table made me feel very welcome and the presentations passed off well. Fortunately, Paul didn't insist that I should make his speech!

All the same, I was glad when David Frost took us back to the office in his Mercedes. It isn't every day that I survey the world from the top of the heap, and I'm not sure that it'd be very comfortable if I had to do it every day. Still now it's over, I can confess that, although it started as a fraught day, it didn't end badly at all!

London

You'll never guess where I've spent the last few days — the wilds of Scotland! Only a few people know about Paul's Scottish farm, but I've been to see it — which is more than Paul's yet done!

The farm is called High Park and it's near Campbeltown, miles from the normal places you'd expect to find a Beatle. There are four hundred acres of nothing but sheep and wind, with a farmhouse in the middle of it all. Paul bought the place without even going to look at it and craftily didn't go near it, waiting until everyone will have forgotten who owns it.

A week or two ago Paul asked me to go up and survey the place and tell him what it's like. He wanted to knock down the old house and build a new house on the land, so could I pick a site for it? Up I went on the overnight train, quite pleased to have a break from London and booked into the local hotel at Campbeltown. There was no chance of staying in the farmhouse; it hasn't been lived in for about five years and I'm not the pioneer type!

I went and walked over the land the next day and, believe me, the Scots know a thing or two about building. There's not another place on the farm you could put up a house without it being blown out to sea. I don't know how the sheep manage to stand upright!

Since Paul's taken it into his head to use the place as some sort of retreat, I went to have a look at the inside of the house. It's middling-to-awful! There's nothing in the way of modern conveniences except a telephone and a low-suite toilet (you might be blown off a high one, I suppose). The floors are stone, weeping with damp, and the walls are mainly covered in chocolate brown paint . Somebody took most of the furniture and kitchen equipment; the only thing in the whole place is a pile of ancient potato boxes in one of the barns. I took a few snapshots and dashed back to the taxi where John, the local driver, was waiting patiently for me and wondering why townies were so interested in the old farm all of a sudden.

Back here in London, I had the pictures developed and showed them to Paul.

"It looks really groovy," he commented.

"It's bloody awful, Paul. There's nothing there at all but wind and sheep. The house hasn't been lived in for years."

Sometimes Paul is drawn towards the primitive; it must be a reaction to being surrounded by luxury most of the time, like eating chips as a change from caviar. His idea was simple: "Look, I like the sound of this place. Let's go up."

"You couldn't go and stay in the hotel. They'd recognize you in five seconds."

Paul thought for a moment. "All right then, just arrange for some second-hand furniture to be put in: beds, cooker, that sort of thing. Any old formica-topped table will do for the kitchen, but make sure that you put in clean bedding."

So the arrangements are made; now Paul and Jane are setting off to spend a few days at the farm and they want me to go along. I don't think I'll be very good at the Boy Scout life, but it might be fun. After all, if the awfully simple life turns out to be simply awful, I can always go back to stay at the hotel — which is more than Paul could do!

London

Well, here we are back from our few days at High Park and I'm still in the land of the living. When we set off I didn't think very much of the idea of roughing it on the moors, but in the end I had a marvellous holiday!

Paul, Jane and I flew up to Macrihanish, where I'd arranged for John, the local taxi-driver, to pick us up. The road to the farm became more and more lonely and I could tell that Paul and Jane were getting really excited at the thought of being able to walk outside without being mobbed by crowds of teenagers. Wait till they see the farmhouse, I thought.

To reach High Park, we had to drive through Low Park Farm and as we went past the farmhouse there, someone waved in our direction.

"That'll be Ian," remarked John. "He said he'd call by this evening to see if you're all right."

Paul and Jane love the farmhouse, despite (or because of?) its lack of any sophistication. They spent the first hour rummaging around discovering things, calling to each other when they found something especially interesting. I never knew old junk could be so fascinating

The farm hasn't been used for years and there are piles of old machinery lying around, left by the last owners, I suppose. The sheep we saw grazing on the land belong to Ian at Low Park Farm, who keeps an eye on the place in exchange.

In the evening we were sitting round the formica-topped table when there was a knock at the door. Our first visitor. It could only be Ian; Beatles fans would have used a battering ram.

"Come in', yelled Paul. A cheerful weatherbeaten face under a greasy cap peered round the door.,

"Hello, Ian. We were expecting you. Come and have a seat."

Ian said something in the broadest Scots accent you could imagine. Paul and I looked at each other, wondering what we ought to say. Jane looked away to avoid meeting our glance.

"Yeah," I ventured.

It was obviously the right answer. Ian said something else.

"Sure," replied Paul, trying to keep his face straight.

Stifling her laughter, Jane took herself off into the other room. After a couple more useless exchanges, with Paul and me watching Ian's face to try to work out whether we were meant to say yes or no, I could see that Ian was beginning to laugh too.

Paul admitted defeat. "Ian, we can't understand a word you're saying!"

Everyone burst out laughing, especially Ian. Jane came back from the other room and we introduced ourselves. Ian's a lovely man. He told us where to walk (and where not to walk) and promised that he and Isobel, his housekeeper, would be around if we needed any help. I'm sure it amused him to see us all playing at farms! Ian left very late, by which time we'd all totally fallen in love with the place.

The next morning, we took stock of the furniture. The one thing we needed most was something to sit on, so we went exploring again. In the bar we came across a pile of old potato boxes, all marked "Sharp's Express" and up in the rafters were a couple of the most disgusting filthy old mattresses I've ever seen. Paul's eyes lit up.

"Hey, I've got a great idea, a fabulous idea. Call John up and get him to take you down to Campbeltown. Get a great bag of long nails and a couple of hammers. We're going to build our own furniture!

When I came back, Paul and Jane were out in the yard, beating one of the old mattresses with sticks, and looking decidedly grey. The state of those mattresses beggared description!

"What are we doing exactly?" I asked.

"I've designed a settee for the kitchen out of Sharp's Express!"

We used the old potato boxes to build a base and a back. Then we put the mattresses on top and hey presto! one settee. But we don't call it a settee; it's a Sharp's Express!"

We didn't stop there, either. The spirit of Chippendale and Hepplewhite entered us and we made some cupboards to stand beside the beds and some more for under the kitchen sink — all out of Sharp's Express boxes. The next time I went into town I bought some paint and we painted all the cupboards — but not the Sharp's Express settee. That was left as raw wood.

A lot of wood left over from the potato boxes went into the Aga cooker. It's an antique in its own right and an absolute sod to light. Even when it was going it smoked all over the kitchen, but Paul liked the atmosphere so he insisted that we always kept it burning. I didn't mind if the bloody thing went out and nobody noticed! Jane cooked our meals on a horrible old electric cooker which we'd picked up cheap. She's a super cook and you'd never know what a primitive kitchen she was working in, but I wish they weren't on to this vegetarian scene. At the end of a week I thought I'd go stark raving mad if I saw another plate of cauliflower cheese!

After a day or two, we all decided we needed a bath. Since we'd decided that we'd solve our own problems, we didn't want to go down to Ian and Isobel, so we looked around. Outside there was a big old dairy with a huge stainless steel trough in the middle of the floor.. It was on a plinth about four feet from the ground and it was about three feet deep. It definitely had possibilities.

"I've got it," said Paul. "We'll rig this up as a bath. All we need is a stepladder!"

So we switched on the water (thank God for immersion heaters) and filled the trough. Then we found a stepladder and took it in turns to climb up into our bath. The funny thing was that when you were in the bath you couldn't see out nor could anyone else see you. All the same, Paul and I stood guard outside the door while Jane had her bath — not that there was anyone around to see!

What a marvellous time we had. It's so peaceful being away from the crowds and the pressure, just walking on the hills, or helping Ian dip his sheep. Paul's batteries are certainly recharged. I think it's one of his best ideas ever to buy the farm.

Alas, it was over all too soon, and John brought the taxi over to take us back to the airport. Still, Paul and Jane want to come again; I hope I'm invited too. Jane wrapped all the food which would keep in polythene bags and stored it carefully in the kitchen cupboards. Then it was goodbye to Sharp's Express and hello to Beatlemania again.

London

Here I am back in civilization after another week with Paul and Jane at High Park. It's just the same as we left it, same old Sharp's Express settee, same old cooker, same old horrible Aga. The only modern aid to living that Paul has put in is a television, but we didn't watch that much. It felt a bit like cheating.

It's so remote and peaceful up at the farm, and such a change from the stresses of Beatle life. The local people respect Paul's privacy. He can even go down to Campbeltown for an occasional visit without being hassled. As long as she doesn't stay too long.

Martha loves it, of course. She's a very city-bred Old English Sheepdog; I don't think she knows much about life outside Paul's home in St. John's Wood! It must have been at High Park that she first even caught sight of a sheep. All the same, she's endowed with a full set of sheepdog instincts, as the sheep could tell you. One sight of them and she was off, trying to round them up, but I think she ended up more exhausted than the sheep!

We did a little bit of "decorating" this time. All that chocolate brown paint makes the farmhouse look like the inside of an Aero bar. Paul at last decided that he'd had enough of it, so he went down to Campbeltown and bought lots of packets of colored pens. The three of us spent the next few hours just drawing little doodles in all these colors, spreading them all over the wall and trying the relieve the gloom!

I did put my foot into it once, though — or my hand. There's a little lake on the farm (well, I think it's on Ian's bit, really) and we borrowed an old rowing boat to go for a trip. We didn't get very far — it's more of a pond than a lake— but it was very pleasant just idling along with one hand trailing in the water while Paul did the rowing. For a change, the wind wasn't blowing and the sun was shining.

Suddenly my hand caught on a bit of weed, so I casually pulled and a large water plant came up roots and all. I as about to throw it back when Jane really delivered me a lecture. Did I know that plants are living creatures and that I'd just killed one, that sort of thing. I suppose she's right, but she did go on for a bit too long about it. Still, I'm forgiven now and we're the best of friends. I'm glad about that, because I think Jane's one of the world's really sweet people.

I don't think any of the other Beatles have seen High Park; Paul keeps it really exclusive, even though it isn't exactly the Ritz. It's a privilege to have a holiday up there with Paul and Jane.

Nice

Well, here I am in Nice, of all places — and very nice too. Oh, I'm not on holiday; not officially, that is. This is one of Brian "treats', which he sometimes springs on me. He's a funny guy; on one hand getting a rise out of him is like getting blood out of a stone; on the other hand, he's likely to whisk me off across the world at five minutes" notice if he thinks I need a change of scenery. I never know when this is going to happen: one minute I'm working away at the office, head stuck in telephone directories and railway timetables, the next I'm told to drop everything and take off to some exotic resort — only to find that I'm not really needed but that Brian thinks I need a rest!

At least I had a day or two to get ready this time. Brian's been in the South of France for a few days, holidaying with his mother and father at Cap Estelle. Now, I know that Brian can't leave work alone for five minutes, so it isn't any surprise to me when he came into my office before he left and told me that he wanted me to fly over with some papers after he'd been away for a while.

"I've just got to go through these papers, Alistair. If you bring them out on Friday, we'll work right through Saturday and that should bring us up to date."

"Is this really necessary, Brian?" said I, thinking that my weekend had just gone for a burton, never mind Brian's holiday.

"Oh, absolutely vital. We must go through those papers. You bring them out to me on Friday. Wendy Hanson will have them ready for you."

Well, I thought, my job's to do what Brian thinks necessary, and if he thinks it's absolutely vital, then it's absolutely vital, whether I think so or not.

"All right, Brian. There's a few things I've got to do in the office on Friday, so I'll come to France on the night flight on Friday. Don't bother with a hotel room for Friday night, I'll be all right."

True to my faithful word, yesterday's dawn saw me touching down at Nice Airport, feeling really frowsty and sticky. All I really wanted to do was have a bath and a shave and change out of my city clothes, which made me feel like a sparrow among budgies as I walked through the crowds of tanned vacationers. Of course, it was raining in London, so the weather is a pleasant change, at least.

The first surprise came when I saw a chauffeur holding a placard with my name on high above his head. The second was the Rolls-Royce waiting outside the door of the terminal. This is better than a black taxi, I thought. More than that, the chauffeur had his instructions. "Mr.Epstein said that I'm to take you to the hotel by the coast road, the Corniche, because he doesn't think you've done that before."

That really was a trip, with the sea glinting in through the tinted windows of the Rolls, and an opulent smell of crushed pound notes wafting into my nostrils. I know that none of this is mine, but if it all ends tomorrow I can say that I've done so much and seen so much that I'd never have dreamed about if I'd stayed in the timber yard in Liverpool. Eat it up while you can, Alistair, you work hard enough for it, I thought.

At the hotel, the doorman swept me inside and had me conducted to a suite which was all ready for me. Then followed a large breakfast with Brian and a really intensive work session; we worked all through the morning. At lunchtime, Brian said, "Come on, Alistair, let's have lunch with Mummy and Daddy."

"Right, Brian, you've got to let me buy you a drink."

"OK."

"What are you having? Gin and tonic. Er, two gin and tonics, please."

The barman poured the drinks and I pulled out my money.

"I'm sorry, monsieur."

"What do you mean, you're sorry?"

"I cannot accept your money, monsieur. Monsieur Epstein's orders."

I turned round and there was Brian sitting back with a huge grin on his face. He'd only instructed every member of the hotel staff I was likely to come across that I'm to be given everything I ask for and under no circumstances am I to be allowed to pay for anything whatsoever!

Back we went to work all afternoon and that was followed by dinner with Brian's parents, marvellous people. I was just beginning to feel the effects of a pretty sleepless night on Friday when Brian said, "Right, we're going off to the Casino. Would you care to join us?" I didn't want to miss this; I've never been in a French casino before and I know that Brian's a great gambler, the perfect companion to break the ice (or the bank) with in a casino.

Off we went in the Rolls, sweeping up to this great palace of a casino. We had to show our passports and pay two francs, which gave us life membership! Brian even insisted on paying that and, as we were walking in, he slipped an English fiver into my hand and said, "Go and back number sevens for me with that. Have a ball." So I backed number sevens until I'd lost all my money, while Brian went off to play on the big money table. I don't know how he did, but he doesn't look too cleaned out this afternoon.!

Here I am, then, having arrived back at the hotel at three in the morning and slept in very late this Sunday morning. Now I'm relaxing on the terrace before having a leisurely lunch and catching the afternoon flight back to drizzly old London. I know people say a lot of very hard things about Brian, but very few people know how warm and generous he can be. I think perhaps he finds difficulty relating to people on equal terms, so he feels he has to make them have a good time on his account. But he needn't with me. I've worked for and with Brian since he was just a record shop proprietor in Liverpool and for all his sudden whims and squally rages, I wouldn't want to work for anyone else.

6
CHAPTER

London

I sometimes wake in the night and wonder where I'd be now if I'd accepted Brian's offer of two-and-a-half per cent of the Beatles way back in 1961!

Someone came up to me at a party the other day and actually suggested that I could make a great deal of money on my own account out of the boys by leaking information to the press or doing various favours for hangers-on. No way. All these guys are my friends, Brian most of all, and, anyway, I don't do so badly. All my accommodation, all my travelling and a lot of my entertainment is paid for and everything's first class, naturally. Besides, I know well that Brian would sniff out betrayal like a terrier catching a three-legged rat. I'd be a fool to try it.

Enough of that.

Wendy Hanson is Personal Assistant to Brian on the boys" current tour of the States, and she found an entirely new sort of problem the other day.

They'd been gone about three days, all seemed to be going smoothly and our London office was unusually quiet after all the frantic rush of their departure. But peace and quiet never last long at NEMS. My secretary came into my office bearing a Western Union cable addressed to me. This couldn't be very urgent, I thought, or they'd have phoned.

The cable said, "Please send urgently supply of Lark cigarettes to next venue. Love, Wendy." I did a double take and then burst out laughing. Poor Wendy. She's a non-smoker and she doesn't realize that Lark cigarettes are actually made in the United States! I'd been having a laugh about the fact that all the boys smoke the same brand of cigarettes. It's as if one of them had bought a Rolls-Royce and that made all the others want a Rolls-Royce. But when I pointed this out, they said that they all like the flavor of Larks better than British cigarettes. Fair enough.

I didn't act at once, because I was due to ring Brian in the States that afternoon, anyway. I could tell Wendy that Larks are American cigarettes and she could just send Mal round to buy them at the nearest tobacconist or drug store or whatever they call them over there.

Sure enough, I spoke to Wendy, but I'd hardly begun to explain when she roared with laughter and stopped me. "Yes I know, Alistair, but the boys insist that the Larks they buy over here aren't the same as the ones at home."

If the boys said so, then that was that. Nothing else would do and she'd been told to get me to send an ample supply over at once. Out went the office boy to buy a couple of thousand Larks, while I contacted my friends at TWA to arrange the quickest possible delivery of this precious cargo, thinking that this time the boys had gone just a little over the top!

When the cartons of cigarettes arrived, I picked one up, wondering idly whether they changed flavor on the Transatlantic trip because of air pressure in the hold of the plane, or something like that. There must be something about them that made them different, otherwise we'd really be carrying coals to New-castle. At this rate, if the boys ever toured Alaska, I'd be sending out ice-packs!

Suddenly the label on the carton caught my eye. These Lark cigarettes were American, all right, but they were blended and packed in Switzerland, not the US. So the mystery was solved, and it wasn't a case of the boys being over- fussy, after all. The taste really is different. They were quite relieved to find out that English Larks are not the same as American Larks because, to be fair, they had felt a bit pernickety when they complained, but they were sure that there was something different about an American Lark!

London

Yes, the Beatles are back in the UK, not that you'd have really noticed in the office that they were away. We've been so busy catching up with a backlog of work that after the first few days it was easy to forget that the boys were in the United States — apart from our lark with the cigarettes, of course.

I've just finished doing a little job for George, by the way. A few days before the boys were due to re-turn, I received a two-page handwritten letter from George headed, "Somewhere in America, Sunday the Something." A lot of it was general chat about the tour, but he also enclosed a photo of himself pulling a horrible face and making a two-fingered gesture at the camera. Some quick-on-the-draw press photog-rapher had caught him in an unguarded moment and the result has been published in an American mag-azine. George reckons that it's the most hilarious picture he's ever seen of himself — he often looks rather serious on official photos — and so he tore the picture out and sent it to me with a very special re-quest. I was to track down the negative and have a life-size copy printed, to be mounted on hardboard and screwed on to the outside of his front door.,

What a job! Where the hell was I to start, as I didn't even know which magazine the cutting had come from. It was just a slow, steady task, phoning press cutting services and agencies, asking friends in Fleet Street to contact their American opposite numbers, and generally sifting through the haystack until the needle showed up. It took more than a week to find, but once we'd bought the negative it was easy to have the print done and waiting for George's return.

George was absolutely knocked out by the effect when he saw it, but I think it's a picture for close friends only and not for official release to the fan club! He He wants to fix it on his bathroom door now!

London

A few weeks ago George walked into my office, plonked himself down and said, "How about that pic-ture you had enlarged for me being my Christmas card, Alistair?"

Part two of the exercise! I've had a pile of them printed — not life-size! — with the message reading "why don't you . . .?" I don't know what his friends will think of it, but it's an original way of spreading goodwill. And this morning I got my card from him with the added message, "To Alistair, without whom it would not have been possible."

London

I fix things for John and Paul and I often fix things for George, but I very rarely seem to get involved with Ringo's requests. I think this is because Ringo's really a very easily satisfied character. You can see this in the way that he sits at the back of the band, steadily drumming away and never thrusting himself into the limelight. He seems to feed off all the adoration less than the others do.

Still, when Ringo does want something, naturally I do my best to come up with it, but somehow there's often a problem with the things I do for him. Take the pool table, for instance. Last month, Ringo came back from the tour of the States and asked me, "Alistair, have you ever heard of a game called pool?"

"Yes, I think so," I replied uncertainly.

"We've been playing it in America," he said, "and it's a knockout game. I'm having a party on Friday and I want a pool table with all the gear, balls, cues, you know."

"No problem," said I, and turned to the telephone directory, thinking this would be an easy one.

The first place I tried was George Riley's, the billiard table maker. They were very snooty on the phone. "We don't make pool tables. It's an American game."

"I know it's an American game, but I want to buy a pool table."

"You won't find a manufacturer in England. I've no idea where you'll get one. Sorry." The only other billiard table maker I could find gave me the same reply.

Now this is where the Fixit circle of contacts comes in useful. It's not so much who you know as who who you know knows. It doesn't matter if something's done through a friend of a friend of a friend as long as it gets done. I nurture contacts like delicate plants, just in case one day I might have to ask them a favor, and many of them become good friends.

But here was a real problem that no contact seemed able to solve. I couldn't have the table shipped from the States in time for the Friday party and there wasn't anyone in business in this country who was able to help. At last I rang a guy called Larry Langley, who's head of the London branch of Trans-World Airways, a really good pal.

"Larry, I've got a problem. I need a pool table."

"Oh, yeah. Try phoning this guy at the American officers club in Piccadilly. He'll be able to help you."

So I rang this American. "Oh Jeez, no, no idea. Try ringing this guy at the PX at Uxbridge."

The next call was to Uxbridge. "Oh no, I'd let you have one if I could, but we just don't carry them. The guys here play on the station tables, they don't need their own. All I can tell you is that the ones we use are made by Brunswick."

Off to Brunswick. "Sorry, the only pool tables in the country are held in bond in Dublin. We can sell you one, but it'll take a week to get it out of bond and have it shipped over to you."

"That's no good. I've got to have it installed in a house in Hampstead the day after tomorrow."

"Oh no, absolutely impossible. There's no way we can possibly do that."

At last I did something I very rarely do. I used Beatlepower at full blast.

"Well, I'll be perfectly honest with you. It's for Ringo Starr of the Beatles."

The attitude suddenly changed. "Oh, that's different. We'll send it over with two fitters and it'll be ready for Mr Starr to play on by Friday evening."

And so it was.

Over the Irish Sea

I've been across the water in my usual disguise of young businessman, doing some fixing for John. Now I'm flying home over the Irish Sea being treated like royalty by Aer Lingus.

It all started during a session with the boys. John laid down his guitar and casually said,, "Alistair, I want you to buy me an island."

Thinking that it was the usual Lennon joke, I replied, "Right, John. What do you want: The Isle of Wight, the Isle of Man, a Caribbean Island?"

He said, "No, I'm absolutely serious. I need to have a place entirely of my own. I want an island with a fresh water supply. I want to build a house on it to get some peace and privacy. Oh, and it mustn't be more than about two hours from London."

This was a ludicrous idea, it seemed to me. Try putting a circle round London with a radius of two hours" travel and what do you find inside it? Not much in the way of islands! But they are always asking me to find weird places and exotic things. For instance, George once decided he'd like to live in a church. By the time I'd found one that was for sale, he'd gone off the idea of sleeping on an altar.

Anyway, the island is quite a natural idea for John. Having a lot of water around him and total privacy from the hordes of fans and followers appeals to him very much. It sounds like a perfect hideaway. Not even Beatles" fans will want to row or swim over miles of freezing water to him! I'm Mr Fixit, so naturally I said, "OK, John. I'll see what I can do." and went away thinking. "Where the hell do I find an island that someone is willing to sell, within two hours" travel from London?

I went to see some of the big estate agents in London and they hadn't really got anything. I often deal with them — under my own name, because the prices would rise astronomically if they knew that I am acting for the Beatles. They're used to my odd requests, but even they raised their eyebrows a bit when I told them what I wanted this time.

As you know, I get every daily newspaper on my desk each morning and the first thing I always look at is the personal ads in *The Times*. I read these because I'm on the lookout for the oddball things that the boys might fancy to buy or find out about. Oddly enough, about three days after John asked me to buy him an island, an advertisement appeared in *The Times*'s personal column which said something like, "Island for sale off the west coast of Ireland. The Westport Harbour Board will hold a public auction ..."

At first I thought, "Marvellous!" Then I thought, "This is a trick. This is Lennon playing a Lennon on me." It was just too much of a coincidence to find an island so quickly. So I phoned Cynthia Lennon and asked her if she knew whether John was plotting something. She swore that he wasn't and that John really did want an island; it wasn't a complicated practical joke.

There was a telephone number in the advertisement for a firm called Browne, who are the local Westport auctioneers. Still thinking that it might yet be a Lennon trick (an auctioneer named Browne in County Mayo?), I rang, and a wild Irish voice answered. Sure enough, it was genuine, and they were auctioning the island on the day after Saint Patrick's day.

There wasn't much time before the auction, so at once I flew to Ireland, drove across to County Mayo and went to have a look at the island. It's called Dorinish and is in Clew Bay, which is a huge bay containing 365 islands — one for every day of the year! The furthest out, next stop America, is Clare Island, legendary burial ground of the old kings of Ireland, while Dorinish is just about the last but one.

It took about an hour and a half to reach Dorinish, by way of a sticky mudbank (now I know how flies feel when they land on fly-paper) in a little boat with an outboard motor, manned by another wild Irishman.

I wandered all over the island, which is really two islands connected by a sand and pebble spit, and I took a lot of snapshots. There are about thirty acres, mainly level, lovely beaches, and a fresh water spring. It really is perfect on a sunny day, but the winds whip in straight from the Atlantic — not good for my creaking back! The only sign that there has ever been habitation on it is a pile of stones which once was a pilot's cottage in the days of sail. The Westport Harbour Commission had given up hopes of being prosperous enough to need a pilot and they were selling off the island as surplus to requirements.

I rushed back to London, had the photographs quickly developed and took them out to John at Kenwood, his house in Weybridge, on the Friday morning. He took one look and cried, "That's it! I've got to have it! Go and buy it for me, Alistair!

The snag was that the auction was on Saturday, the next day. I couldn't get a flight at such short notice, so I was forced to take the boat train from Euston to Holyhead — which didn't appeal to me at all.

There was one more problem — money. The boys carry very little cash; there isn't much opportunity for them to spend it casually. Neither are their houses riddled with wall safes, as you might suppose. John's attitude is, "You worry about that" I never carry any."

I rang Ireland to see whether they would accept a check (of course, still in my character as Alistair Taylor, London entrepreneur). They would only accept a check certified by a bank. I can't say that I blame them. If they'd known I was buying for the Beatles, it would have been different — and vastly more expensive. Still, sometimes I'm tempted to cut through all the red tape and snootily say, "Do you know whom I represent?" But if I did, I'd be out of a job; everyone would find out who I am, you see.

I then had to think very hard. All the banks were closed and there was no chance of having a check certified before the auction. I had only two hours before I was due to meet the travel agent with the tickets at Euston and board the train. There wasn't even time to book a cabin on the boat from Holyhead. I rang my brother-in-law in Dublin and said, "Paddy, can you help me out?" He answered, "I'd love to, but my bank's in England." Oh no! Did no one have money in the right place?

It was up to me to do something. I had one check in my own checkbook, a little spare cash, and nothing else. But when John knows about something and wants it, he has to have it and no excuses. So I rang Clive Epstein, Brian's brother, in Liverpool and we came to a last-minute arrangement that his chauffeur would be on Crewe station with eight hundred pounds as the train drew in. The chauffeur would hold a newspaper above his head and I was to jump off and identify myself to him, pick up the money and leap aboard the train again. Problem solved. It sounded easy. After all, there couldn't be many people walking about on Crewe station at midnight with rolled-up newspapers above their heads.

Lesley decided she'd come along for the trip, so early in the evening we climbed on board the train at Euston, found our first-class compartment, drew the blinds and tried to ignore the sounds of drunken Irishmen rolling beer bottles down the corridor. It's strange being in a train at night, like being in a little box hurtling through the countryside. When I peered out, it was dark and witchy. I didn't go out into the corridor; two Irishmen were being sick out of the window and I wanted to be well upwind of them.

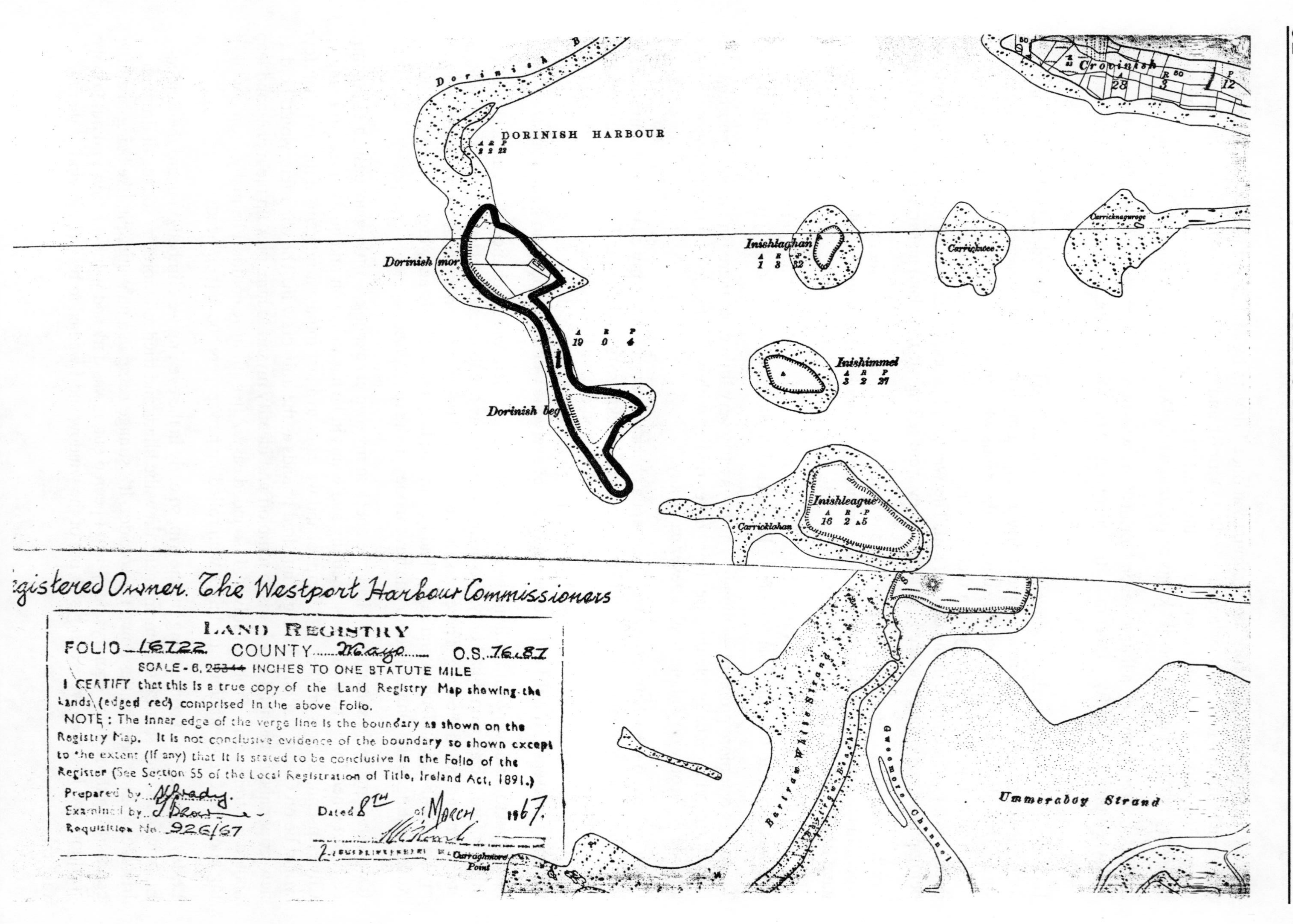
DORINISH HARBOUR
Dorinish mor
Dorinish beg
Inishlaghan
Inishimmel
Inishleague
Carricklohan
Crovinish
Gweemore Channel
Ummeraboy Strand
Bartraw White Strand
gistered Owner. The Westport Harbour Commissioners
LAND REGISTRY
FOLIO 16722 COUNTY Mayo O.S. 76.87
SCALE - 6 INCHES TO ONE STATUTE MILE
I CERTIFY that this is a true copy of the Land Registry Map shewing the lands (edged red) comprised in the above Folio.
NOTE: The inner edge of the verge line is the boundary as shown on the Registry Map. It is not conclusive evidence of the boundary so shown except to the extent (if any) that it is stated to be conclusive in the Folio of the Register (See Section 55 of the Local Registration of Title, Ireland Act, 1891.)
Prepared by
Examined by
Requisition No. 926/67
Dated 8th of March 1967.

The train rolled on and I relaxed until the ticket inspector came round. I showed him our tickets and asked, "Can you tell me what time the train gets into Crewe?"

He said, "It doesn't. We don't stop at Crewe."

I laughed. "You must be kidding me. Everything stops at Crewe."

He replied, "No, we stop outside Crewe to change drivers, but we miss the station completely."

Oh my God! Next stop Holyhead, with my money man walking up and down Crewe station with a rolled-up newspaper all night. There was nothing to do but sit there until the train drew into Holyhead. There were two hours until the boat sailed and it seemed hopeless. So we walked across the wide platform and straight up the gangplank on to the boat.

I shot off to grab a cabin and when we were settled in, Lesley summed up the situation to me. "Is there any point in going? You've got no money, one check , which is uncertified anyway, and so how are you going to buy an island?"

"Well," I said, "somehow it's got to be done. I'm not Mr Fixit for nothing." But I had no ideas this time. Something had to turn up. The Beatles are not exactly hard taskmasters; they just expect things to be done, whatever the cost and effort.

The boat was due to sail at two o'clock and at about ten to two I had a funny feeling and I thought, "I'm going to have one last look on the quayside." So I walked over to the side of the boat and there on the lonely vast quayside, under the only naked lamp, was one solitary guy, standing there — with a newspaper under his arm! I hurried down the gangplank and as I reached the bottom, he just looked at me and held the newspaper above his head! I was saved.

He'd driven halfway to Crewe, then telephoned the station to check when the train arrived. He'd just turned round and made for Holyhead, collecting two speeding tickets on the way, I believe. The poor guy had been there for an hour, just waiting, on the off-chance I'd appear. He deserves a medal for initiative.

That was fine. I identified myself and he gave me the eight hundred pounds for the deposit. So we set sail for Ireland in a little less of an Irish stew and able to snatch a few hours of welcome sleep. We drove across to Westport in plenty of time and arrived in the middle of the morning. The sale was not until two o'clock so we checked into a hotel and I went off to have a word with the auctioneers.

Mr Browne, the auctioneer, had his office in a milliner's shop, full of drapery and haberdashery. It could only happen in Ireland! Mrs Browne recognized me as the man who had been there a few days previously. "Oh, you're back," she said. "Mr Browne isn't too well at the moment. You didn't meet him last time you were here, but he wants to meet you now. He was educated in London, you see. Would you mind very much popping upstairs and having a chat with him?"

"No, of course. I'd love to," I volunteered, so off I went up the stairs, and there was an old chap sitting in a wing-back chair with a shawl around his shoulders.

"Will you have a John Jameson?"

What a pleasant way to greet a guest! "Love to."

Out came two great slugs of Irish whiskey and he asked me all about London and how it had changed. He'd been to college in the Strand and he told me tales of London forty years ago. You know me, I can sit and listen all day. We were getting on fine, when he looked sharply at me and said, "Do you really want this island?"

"Yes, I do, very much," I replied. "I'm only a young businessman and I can't afford very much money, but I'd love it."

"What can you afford to pay?'

This was asking too much, too soon. I decided to be a little vague: "Well really, quite honestly, I've no idea what it's worth, but I can go up to about £2,000, maybe a little more."

"Right," he said. "Now I'll tell you in strict confidence. The reserve price is £1,550, but there's a syndicate from Manchester and one from Cork who'll be pushing the price up. I like the look of you, so let me give you a tip. My son Michael is the only solicitor in Westport. Let him do the bidding for you this afternoon."

"OK. That's fine by me," I agreed.

Mr Browne picked up the phone and summoned Michael, who is a shy, quiet young man. He agreed to do the bidding. All I had to do was watch in silence — which is sometimes the hardest thing of all. I took my leave of Mr Browne and Michael and went off to have a thoughtful lunch.

After lunch, Lesley was so nervous that she went off to have her hair done! When I arrived at the auction, it was quite crowded; obviously there was a lot of interest in the island. It was easy to recognize the businessmen amongst the local onlookers; their suits and ties made them stand out like magpies among sparrows. Just before it all began, Michael appeared in the doorway. Without a word, he stood at the back near the doorway, opened a newspaper and disappeared behind it. All I could see were his fingers and his legs. Very reassuring.

Browne senior described the island in the greatest detail. He went on and on about its virtues and its potential for development. Eventually he started the bidding at £1,000. Another ten minutes passed. "It's worth much more than this ...reliable freshwater spring...grazing for cattle ...another bid, gentlemen, please."

£1,200. And so it went on slowly, in fifties and hundreds, with old Browne selling the virtues of the place like mad and the price inching up, with ten minutes or more between bids. "I'm going to have to withdraw it ...it's worth much more...you don't appreciate its value..."

Finally the bidding crept up to £1,500. Off he went again and I started to get sweaty palms. I knew that it was reaching the minimum reserve price, and Michael still had not moved from behind his newspaper. Would he ever bid? Were the Brownes trying to con me, somehow?

Another ten minutes of hard sell from old Browne was followed by: "Now, any further bids?"

For a moment there was silence, then from behind Michael's newspaper came a quiet Irish voice: "£1,550'.

Browne senior slammed gavel down at once and cried, "Done! Sold to the gentleman with the newspaper for £1,550!"

There was a gasp around the room at this sudden end to the auction. I looked around for Michael but he was nowhere to be seen. He'd slipped away through the door as soon as he'd made the clinching bid. For all that anyone knew, the island could have been sold to the Invisible Man! There was an uproar from the Manchester syndicate, who apparently wanted to open a casino on the island, but there was nothing to be done. It was all sewn up.

I put down my eight hundred pounds cash deposit and the island was mine (or rather, John's).

I rang John, who is very happy, especially about the price. Then all the Brownes" friends came in and I had my first Guinness in Ireland. I don't remember a lot about the night! Apparently the island has the finest grazing in Clew Bay, so everybody was offering me money to allow their animals to graze!

Today, feeling fairly wrecked, I left Lesley, who's staying in Ireland for a short holiday, and boarded the plane home — first class of course. There were only half a dozen people in the cabin and it was very peaceful. After we'd taken off, I noticed that the stewardess kept looking at me. Suddenly she came up and said, "Excuse me, aren't you the Mr Taylor who's bought the island?"

I answered, "Yes, that's me." Wow! I'm an instant VIP. All the other passengers turned round and welcomed me to the Irish landowning classes! Now I'm being treated like a lord and people are wondering where I got the money from and what I'm going to do with the island. I wonder what John is going to do with it?

7

CHAPTER

London

Ringo went off from Heathrow today to join the rest of the boys on their world tour. Wasn't that a piece of bad luck for him — to have to go into hospital to have his tonsils removed just as the band was due to start this huge tour? But I don't expect Jimmy Nicol thinks so. What a break for a professional musician — to get to stand in for one of the Beatles with a list of appearances all over the globe. I only hope he was prepared for the shock of being an insider at a Beatles concert. Only too well do I remember my first visit to one!

Poor old Ringo wasn't looking too well when Brian and I arrived with him at Heathrow this morning. Brian had postponed joining the boys on tour until Ringo was well enough to fly out and the arrangement is that Brian and Ringo can break their journey in the United States to give Ringo a rest. After all, playing in a Beatles concert, even if he doesn't have to sing much, isn't the ideal form of convalescence!

This morning looked like being one of the easy ones. Only one Beatle and one Brian to think about and we'd even managed to arrange a press conference at the airport so Ringo wouldn't be bothered by the usual barrage of questions all the way from his car to the plane. Once more, our friends Pan-Am were looking after us and their representative Whip Waterhouse was hovering nearby, just in case we needed anything.

Would you have believed that anyone's tonsils could be such big news as Ringo's? I don't think even the removal of Prince Charles's tonsils caused such excitement! Brian was in top form, though, handling the questions beautifully and getting the maximum press exposure from Ringo's operation.

It struck me that it would be a good idea to sort out all the passport business while the press conference was going on, so that Ringo could just stand up after it had finished and walk on to the plane without any more fiddling about. Up I crept alongside Ringo's chair, trying to look as inconspicuous as a fly on a currant bun. I reminded Ringo that I'd said last night that I'd collect his passport from him at the airport this morning. Ringo's glum face took on an even glummer expression s he whispered, "I've forgotten it."

"Very funny. Come on, just give it to me, mate."

"I'm telling you the truth, Al. I've forgotten it. Sorry."

"Stop larking about, Ringo. You are larking about, aren't you? Aren't you? No, you aren't. Oh, hell. Just sit tight and I'll see what we can do. Do you know where it is, then?"

"It's somewhere at home, I think. Last time I had it, I put it in the pocket of the suit I was wearing."

"Which one?'

"Don't know. Sorry'

Do you know how many suits a Beatle has? Off I dashed to the phone and dialled Ringo's home number. Thank God, Maureen was in.

"Hello, it's Alistair. I'm at Heathrow with Ringo, but we haven't got his passport. Have you seen it anywhere? He thinks it might be in a pocket of one of his suits."

"Which one?"

"Don't know. Sorry."

"Hold on. I'll go and look."

This was another of those breathless waits that I'm sure I'll never get used to. There were Ringo and Brian with half the world's press waiting to photograph them going up the steps of the plane and if Ringo's passport didn't turn up then they'd have lovely shots of us all going home like gatecrashers chucked out of a party. It didn't bear thinking about, especially as I'm responsible for their travel arrangements. Here's a lesson for you, Alistair. Leave nothing to chance and never let anyone else do what you're responsible for if you can do it yourself. Oh why didn't I check earlier? There's only thirty minutes before the flight. Come on Maureen...please!!!

"Hello, Alistair?"

"Hello, Maureen. Any luck?" Unbearable tension.

"Yes. It was in the pocket of a suit, just like he said."

"Can you get it to me in the next thirty minutes or so, Maureen? His plane's about to leave."

"I'll never get it there by car...Wait! I know! We've got a friend up the road who's got a motorbike. I'm sure he'll bring it if he can."

"OK, Maureen. Best of luck. Bless you. Bye."

There must be certain people who never suffer from ulcers, and I must be one of them — I hope. I've had enough worry in this job to give ulcers to a whole board of directors and my digestion's still holding out! Back at the press conference, I tried to look unconcerned and willed the motorcycle man to do the ton. We'd have paid his fines gladly.

Oh no, final call for Ringo's flight and still no signs of help! What was I to do? A world tour awaited our hero and he couldn't move without a passport. That's it! Confide in Whip Waterhouse of Pan-Am and throw myself on his mercy. Otherwise Jimmy Nicol was going to have to do a few more gigs, and it would be all my fault.

Now, it's a funny thing, but if you or I forgot our passport there'd be no chance of doing anything about it. We'd just miss our flight and lose our holiday. But when a Beatle loses his passport, things are different. "Let's go," said Pan-Am. "We'll work something out to get Ringo into the US and you can put the passport on to the next plane out. It'll catch up with him in a few hours. Just leave it to us."

Off went Brian and Ringo, a little worried about what was waiting at the other end. From the windows of the lounge where we'd held the press conference, I watched them walk over to the 707, climb the steps and give a final wave before the doors closed. The engines roared into a higher pitch and the monster began to taxi to the end of the runway.

The press were taking their last pictures and preparing to pack up and go home. One of the pressmen turned to Whip Waterhouse and said "I hear Ringo's forgotten his passport. How's he going to get by without it?"

Whip paused for a moment and then, with a wry smile, said, "Gentlemen, a Beatle is a Beatle the world over." What a line! I hope that gets into the papers.

At that very moment, the door of the lounge burst open and in rushed Maureen's motorcycling neighbor, clutching the missing passport. Some quick-thinking character gave it to a Pan-Am ground hostess and she held it up against the window just as the jet carrying Ringo and Brian took off in the background. Now there's a picture that should look well over the cornflakes tomorrow morning!

London

What a day! Sometimes I wonder if the boys know how much trouble they can cause in the most casual way. Of course they don't know; it's my job to make sure that the ripples never reach them and I think they'd be genuinely horrified if they knew what is done behind the scenes to make sure that they have everything they want.

Take this morning. From the TV pictures which the News showed tonight you wouldn't think that there was any problem at Heathrow Airport when they went off on this tour. All the fans were neatly shepherded onto the viewing platform of the Queen's Building, a car drew upon the tarmac next to the plane, John, Paul, George and Ringo sprang out, waved to the masses and went straight up the steps on to the jet. Close doors, taxi, take-off, fans go home, another successful operation.

I was at the airport an hour or two early as usual, checking the security and general arrangements and feeling that we were in for an easy time. For once, the boys had decided not to take all their stage equipment on tour with them, but to travel light, with only their guitars and Ringo's snare drum. This made things much easier for me and for Pan-Am. All I had to do was to arrange for all the amps and speakers and full drum-kit to be hired and to be waiting for the boys on arrival at the other end. This is a habit I like them to develop because it means that we don't have to fiddle around while the Customs check every piece of equipment.

There I was, then, in the Pan-Am Clipper Club lounge, when I was called out to meet Big Mal Evans, our roadie. He had a very sheepish grin on his face.

"Sorry, Alistair, but the boys ... er ...changed their minds."

"What do you mean, Mal? Changed their minds about what?"

"About their gear. They want to take their own stuff on the tour."

"It's a bit late now to get it all together, isn't it?" I retorted. "They're due here in about twenty minutes and they'll be taking off as soon as possible. There's not a chance of going all the way back to town in time to get it, thank God, and even if we had it we wouldn't be able to get it on the plane at this short notice. Come and have a drink and we'll tell them later that it wasn't possible to go back and collect it all."

"It's in the van already, Al. Parked outside on the yellow line. I think I just got a parking ticket, too."

I absolutely blew my top. Here we had a fully-loaded plane all ready for take-off and I was expected immediately to find room for a ton of extra luggage which hadn't even been through Customs.

"Tough luck, Mal. It'll have to follow on the next plane. For once they'll have to realize that I can't do the impossible."

"Sorry, Alistair, no go. They say they won't play unless their stuff goes with them on this plane."

Well, I know I'm Mr Fixit and I'm the victim of my own reputation for getting things done against the odds. Anyway, if I started saying things *couldn't* be done there'd soon be a different Mr Fixit at NEMS. Loyalty is one thing, but reality is another. So it was run to the phone and hope that I could conjure up my two miracle workers at Pan-Am, Whip Waterhouse and David Blott. They're marvellous guys who'll do anything for me, as long as it's legal (I think). When they answered, I just put the facts to them and threw myself on their mercy.

"Don't worry, Alistair. We'll see you all right. Go and have a drink and look after putting the boys on to the plane. Their luggage will be aboard, never fear."

And so it was. Even before the boys arrived at the airport, their gear was loaded on to their plane and all was serene. When I greeted them, I was able to tell them they'd have everything they wanted with them.

"Thanks, Al. We knew you could do it."

Thanks, David and Whip. I don't know how they did it. I wonder whose cargo was pulled off the plane at the last minute to make way for ours.

Now to cancel the order for the hire of a complete set of stage equipment which I suppose will be waiting for the boys when they disembark. Never mind. As long as they're happy, the fans are happy and we're still in business.

London

I've lost a genuine live Beatle in the middle of a major international airport! Oh, he's back in the fold now, but through no fault of mine.

Ringo asks for very little from me, but when he does, things often seem to go wrong with the arrangements. Last week, he went off to Corsica on a much-needed holiday with Maureen, Zak, Maureen's mother and the nanny. This was a holiday which he'd organized himself, thank God. Two days later, the phone rang in my office and there was Ringo on a very crackly line. Just about everything that could be wrong was wrong in Corsica and everyone was so upset that he'd decided they had to come home as soon as possible. The problem was that there was no direct flight back to London for nearly a week. I never knew that some parts of Europe were so inaccessible, but I suppose that a Beatle needs a really inaccessible place for his holiday. It wouldn't be much of a break for him on the beach at Southport!

Sit tight, Ringo, says I, and I'll see what I can manage. I'll call you back. Then it was the usual hunt through the address book and a quick call to the plane hire company we use, at Luton Airport. They're used by now to our sudden requests for air transport and they always do their best to lay on their best plane for us — the private jet. Luckily, it was free.

That was one part of the problem solved. The next was to get Ringo out of Corsica. A phone call to our travel agent came up with a flight from Corsica to Paris, due at Orly Airport at eight that evening. Problem solved.

Ringo picked the phone up as soon as it rang, he was so anxious to be home. I told him I'd booked them all tickets on the Orly flight and gave him precise details and made him repeat them to me. These telephone lines are so bad that you can't be sure that you're still talking to the person you started with. All was fine; I'd be waiting for them when they came off the plane, and would conduct them with minimum fuss or publicity to the jet for the flight back to Luton.

All this was pretty routine stuff and all in a day's work for me. I often end up on the other side of the Channel instead of home in my warm flat in the evening. As soon as I walked through the door of the charter company's office I knew there was something wrong. The manager slowly rose from his desk, very red-faced, and announced, "I'm sorry, Mr Taylor. I'm afraid there's no jet available today. It's being serviced up in Chester."

"Marvellous. Do you realize that I have to be at Orly by eight o'clock tonight? What have you got, if you haven't got the jet?"

"There's only the twin prop."

"That'll take all night!"

"If we get you moving now, there's a fair chance, given the right winds, of arriving at Orly a little before eight. But we'll have to move fast."

Oh, what a time it takes to arrange clearance through passport control (no favors at Luton!), pick up a flight plan for the pilot and be cleared for take-off. The minute hand of my watch seemed to zoom round as fast as the second hand. At last we lumbered into the air like a wallowing hippopotamus in contrast to the sleek jet I'd been led to expect.

At least there was nothing at all to do on the air journey but wait for the touch-down — as if that wasn't bad enough. We landed at the far side of Orly (helped by the winds) at five minutes to eight. Luckily, I'd arranged a car to take me over to the terminal, so off I shot. It was ten past eight when I jumped out of the car and dashed into the terminal. If only the winds that had helped me had held up the flight bringing Ringo from Corsica!

No such luck. The arrivals board showed that Ringo's plane had landed. I never knew airport corridors could be so long, as I ran down that one at Orly, finally arriving at the right gate, panting and sweaty, to find no one there but a rather bored-looking Air France ground hostess.

"Oui monsieur, everyone cleared this gate fifteen minutes ago."

I hurried back to the main concourse, my eyes on stalks looking for that unmistakable face. No sign anywhere, not in the concourse, not in the arrival lounge, not in the corridors, not in the gents. This was it, I thought. They've been kidnapped, or torn to pieces by a wandering band of fans and I'll find a ransom note or discarded ring as the only evidence. What was I to do?

Certainly I couldn't search a whole airport alone, so I enlisted come help from Pan-Am and Air France. I think they thought I was a maniac, when I said we had to find a lost Beatle. We split the map of the airport into four and each went to explore our area, searching into all the least likely places you'd expect to find a Beatle.

No luck. After fifteen fruitless minutes, we all met, but everyone had drawn a blank. Air France had checked the passenger manifest and, yes, the party had been on the plane and, no, there hadn't been a flight out to London since the flight from Corsica had landed. They must be in the airport; if they weren't, I might as well book a single ticket to Timbukto, as the man who lost a Beatle wouldn't be flavor of the month back home.

I thanked my valiant helpers, and wandered aimlessly back into the main concourse. If they hadn't left the airport, where were they? Even Mr Fixit was stumped this time! I honestly didn't know what to do next. Call a magician, I suppose.

In the main lounge, I went up to the counter to grab a sandwich and a coffee (I hadn't eaten since lunch-time). As I walked towards the counter, a young women turned away from it holding cups of coffee. I almost bumped into her, and was just about to say "excuse me" when I realized it was Maureen! Oh, weak-at-the-knees relief! She led the way through the crowded lounge and sitting there, looking a bit sorry for himself, was Ringo, with Zak on his knee, surrounded by a few bits of hand luggage! All around them were crowds of people, but not one of them even looked at the Beatle — and this at a time when the very mention of a rumor that they might be in town is enough to stop the traffic in any city in Europe! Miracles do happen.

It turned out that they'd landed and seen no sign of me, so Ringo, with his usual down-to-earth approach, had simply picked up all the luggage, booked them on the first flight to London and retired to the lounge, disgusted by the absence of the reliable Alistair. And not one person recognized him through all this. Ringo soon forgave me when I explained everything, and we had a good laugh about it all on the plane trip home.

Hotel George Cinq, Paris

I'm in Paris, staying at the legendary Hotel George Cinq, living off the fat of the land, and all because someone made a mistake!

I was down at Heathrow this morning, seeing the boys off on the first leg of the European tour. It was the usual howling chaos, with the fans in their thousands screaming from the top of the Queen's Building, the police looking harassed, the press using up flashbulbs as if they were going out of fashion. There was nothing in the world I wanted so much as a hot cup of coffee and a chance to put my feet up back at the office. I'd been at the airport since the early hours of the morning sorting out the last-minute arrangements and making sure that we didn't make the most almighty hash of the security arrangements in front of the cameras.

Bang on time to the minute up purred Brian's Rolls, down whirred the window on the front passenger side and out came Brian's very harrassed-looking face. Above the screaming of the fans and the droning of the engines he yelled to me, "Get on to the plane, Alistair; we've got a problem in Paris. I need you over there now."

It's no use at a time like this saying "But I'm only dressed for the office, just a briefcase in my hand, no topcoat even." or "I haven't got my passport, let alone a ticket." or "But the cat needs to be fed at one o'clock." There's no alternative but to look dutifully eager and resign myself to a day or two in Paris instead of London. Fortunately, my good friend from Air France, Trevor Jones (a fine Gallic name!) was standing nearby and he soon rounded up his team to arrange for me to board the plane, ticketless and passportless as I was, while I yelled to a colleague to tell my secretary where I was bound.

When the plane was in the air and the "No Smoking" light had gone out, I leaned over to Brian and asked him what the problem was.

"Oh, the souvenir brochures aren't ready yet, so I thought you ought to come over to Paris and organize something in their place."

"Sure, Brian, I know lots of printers in Paris," I muttered sarcastically under my breath. At that point, one of the entourage, I forget who, leaned over from the seat in front and casually remarked, "But Brian, the brochures are ready; they came this morning and we had them loaded directly on to the plane. We just forgot to tell you in the rush to the airport."

Brian gave a small grin of apology and amusement. "Oh well, you'll enjoy an evening in Paris with us, Alistair. Remind me to give you some money when we've booked into the hotel." It didn't worry Brian that I had no ticket and no passport and that I was wondering whether I'd be let into France at all or whether I'd be sent back on the plane to Heathrow, where they mightn't let me back into Britain without a passport. I might become the Flying Dutchman of the airways, condemned to fly endlessly from airport to airport, but never allowed to disembark, living on plastic airline food, consuming endless airline boiled sweets and forever slipping packs of airline sugar into my pocket!

As it was, I needn't have worried. Obviously, there had been some talking on the telephone between Heathrow and Orly and my path through Customs and Immigration was smoothed in the usual efficient manner. I wasn't even asked for my ticket or passport at the airport, while everyone at this magnificent hotel clearly expected me. Such is Beatlepower. I don't expect they let President Johnson in without a look at his passport!

So now I'm off shopping in Paris to buy a set of nightclothes suitable for display amongst the denizens of this place. I should think silk is obligatory here. Then dinner, bed and another (I hope) trouble-free trip back to London. It's a hard life, isn't it?

London

Am I still on this planet? After the day I've had, I'm beginning to doubt it.

I had a late night last night and was waking up this morning with a headache and a cup of black coffee when the telephone rang. It was Brian. "Alistair, I've got to go to the States now! If I don't smooth things out, the Beatles are finished."

He was talking to me from his sickbed in Portmeirion. You know the boys are about to leave for a tour of the United States and Brian, who has been very ill, had taken the opportunity to have a short break in this village in the furtherest corner of North Wales. Unfortunately for Brian, the press have splashed over the world's papers this story that John said the Beatles are "more popular than Jesus'. The results have been awful, especially in the Southern states. You'll have seen by now the evening news on the television with film of kids hurling Beatles records on to huge bonfires and politicians and priests thundering threats of divine punishment. Beatlemania has gone into reverse gear with a vengeance over there. It looks as if John would be lynched if he set foot in one of those small townships. With this tour of the States about to happen, Brian was in a hurry to go over as quickly as he could and sort things out — if possible.

When Brian explained all this and I'd looked at a few of the headlines in the papers, I could see his point. You can imagine I didn't have time to finish my coffee or even tidy myself up. This was disaster coming up in the fast lane!

It was terrible timing. It's the peak of the holiday season; Transworld Airlines have gone on strike, which means that Pan-Am are flying out totally full planes; to cap it all, Brian was buried about as far from an international airport as it is possible to be! It was obviously a job for Mr Fixit who, unlike Superman, doesn't need a telephone booth for his act, merely a telephone.

The first steps at least were easy. I "arranged" a seat for Brian on a Pan-Am flight leaving Heathrow this afternoon. Ken Gregory, of Gregory Air Taxis, was to be at Hawarden airport, near Chester, with a light plane to bring Brian down to Heathrow. A chauffeur-driven car was sent to transport Brian from Portmeirion to Hawarden. This was nothing special for me, but I decided to go to Heathrow to have a word with Brian between flights and to be on the spot if trouble developed. And develop it did!

I was relaxing in Pan-Am's Clipper Club lounge, congratulating myself on another job completed, when I was called to the telephone. Ken Gregory was on the line from Hawarden.

"He's not here, Alistair."

Do you know that feeling of shock when your legs go numb and you want to run away anywhere, but can't? That's what I felt. I wanted to run around the lounge screaming in rage.

It took a few seconds to regain control. "But he was supposed to take off half an hour ago!" I gasped. "There's very little time to transfer him to the Pan-Am jet here! Just hang on until he comes. He must come! Take off as soon as you can and I'll sort things out at this end."

At once I got on to Pan-Am. It costs an unbelievable amount to hold an airliner on the tarmac at Heathrow, but they agreed to a few minutes" wait and Air Traffic Control reluctantly consented. But there could be no long delay. Brian must arrive at Hawarden soon.

A few minutes later there was another call from Ken Gregory. "Brian's on his way. His driver got lost in Wales."

This was an enormous relief, but was there time to transfer Brian from the light aircraft to the airliner? All light aircraft flying into Heathrow have to land at South side. To bring Brian from South Side by car and to go through the business of passports and customs would take much longer than Pan-Am could possibly keep their airliner waiting.

So there it was. Brian would miss his plane. God alone knew what would happen to the tour ... and to the Beatles. An idea suddenly struck me. I went to see the head of Air Traffic Control, explained the situation and outlined what would probably happen if Brian did not make that plane. Then I chanced my arm. "Is there any way you could bring Brian's plane down on the main runway and let it taxi right up to the airliner?"

There was some humming and hawing, but at last the man said, "All right, but just this once!"

We were saved, thanks to his incredibly flexible attitude, and to Immigration, who agreed to let Brian's tiny midge come down on the main runway among all the 707s and DC8s. It taxied to the airliner, where I was waiting under the wing. Brian climbed out on to the wing of his plane, as the propellers blew that blue and white spotted scarf which he always wears back over his shoulder. He still didn't know the reason he had landed there and he was sure that he had missed the plane to the States.

"Oh, Alistair, I'm so sorry, and after all your efforts, too. It wasn't my fault, honestly. I wasn't late; the driver got lost in the mountains. Oh well, when's the next plane?"

"If you don't hurry up, Brian, this one'll be gone without you!" I shouted.

"Great! Marvellous!" With a wide grin on his face, Brian ran up the steps as quickly as he could in his fairly weak condition. The attendants stowed his luggage in the hold. All was well.

The door was about to close and the engines were picking up revs, when suddenly Brian's head appeared. "My tablets!" They're in my suitcase. I've got to have them. The doctor says I've to take them every three hours. I'll never last across the Atlantic without them!"

"Which suitcase?" I yelled above the thunder of engines.

"I don't know!"

So we had to have all the suitcases out of the hold and open them there on the tarmac, while the gale from the jets threatened to blow Brian's clothes away. At last, after rummaging away like a stoat in a sack, I found the bottle of tablets and the door finally closed on Brian.

I walked back weak-kneed to the buildings to thank all the officials who has so kindly bent all their rules to save the Beatles" tour. When I talked to the pilot of the light aircraft which had brought Brian down from Hawarden he said that he hadn't been able to believe his order from the control tower to land on the main runway. It had taken six queries and six repeats of the instruction before he had been convinced!

8
CHAPTER

London

Not only does Brian have an exceptional "nose" for a hit, he also is quite good at picking groups, as the last three years prove! We still play the old game of predicting the charts, though, and we were round at Brian's Belgravia flat in William Mews doing it earlier tonight.

I've just been running the rule over a new group called the Silkie; they're a fold group, but I think there's something rather special about them and NEMS is going to sign them up. Brian's just come back from a trip to the States and he asked me to bring the Silkie over to William Mews for a chat about things. He'd arrived home literally minutes before us, and we were unwinding over a drink and generally chatting about the future. As usual, the talk turned to our musical likes and dislikes. Brian suddenly sprang up from his chair and said, "Listen. I'm going to play you a track I've brought back with me from the States. It's going to be a smash hit. The odd thing is it's on a film album. The rest's so-so, but this track's sensational!"

We all duly listened to this very unusual track and when it finished there was a moment's silence. Each of us was waiting for one of the others to make the obvious point. At last, Kev, the bass player piped up: "Well, Mr Epstein, I shouldn't really argue with you, of all people, but it is an instrumental, and how many of those make the Top Ten?"

The rest of us nodded sagely; unless it's by the Shadows, what chance does an instrumental have in the charts? I added, "I must agree with him, Brian. I just don't see it."

"Ah, Alistair, remember "Georgia on my Mind"! Who was right then?" Brian jokingly reminded me. "I think it'll be taken off the album, issued as a single, and that it will be in the Top Ten."

We agreed to differ, five to one against Brian. All the same, I didn't bet him a drink on it this time! It's called "Zorba's Dance'. What a title!

London

Poor old Paul put his foot in it last night. We were all at Abbey Road and the boys were recording, as usual. It was ten o'clock and they were thoroughly fed up because it wasn't going right. There was something missing, but no one could work out what was needed. Everyone was drinking coffee and occasionally throwing an idea into the discussion, but no inspiration had yet come.

Suddenly Paul came up with a good idea. "Do you know what we need? We need a bank of saxes just there and again there." He hummed the tune, showing where the saxes were to go.

"Yes, you could be right," agreed George Martin, ever willing to let the boys have their heads in creating ideas for songs.

The next step was for Mal to ring round to some of the fixers in the music business. These are the agents and contacts who know all the session men, the often uncredited musicians and sometimes they make a very important contribution to a recording. From time to time really famous musicians sit in on sessions, especially for their friends. Take a close look at the credits on the back of some of your album sleeves and you'll see what I mean.

Anyway, we all retired to a grotty little canteen with a coffee vending machine in the corner while the fixers rang around to try and find any saxophonists who might be available for work at ten o'clock at night. Amazingly there seemed to be quite a few and gradually they started to arrive. They were quite a mixed bunch, some looking like classical musicians, some more like down-and-outs, some young and hopeful, others elderly and careworn, each an unknown face with a saxaphone in a case.

Now, I had no idea who the fixers had called, but there's one saxophonist whose face any jazz fan like me could recognize blindfolded in a coal cellar. Yes, the man whose club has made him one of the most famous jazz men in the world — Ronnie Scott. And as Paul and I walked out of the canteen, the door opened and in walked Ronnie Scott, saxophone case in hand! In all my fantasies I never imagined that he would ever turn out at short notice to play as a session man for the Beatles!

His face meant nothing to Paul, who just stared at him without much interest. Before I could say anything, Paul asked, "Are you a sax player?"

Ronnie Scott just grinned and replied, "Well, some people say I am," and walked on down the corridor!

In horror I turned to Paul and whispered, "Paul, do you know who you've just been talking to?"

"Yeah, he's a sax player."

"It's Ronnie Scott!"

"Shit!" Paul's face was a study in surprise. "You're joking! Oh no!"

At once Paul went racing off to catch Ronnie Scott and offer his apologies for not recognizing him. They were soon talking like old friends, so I left them to it and went back to the door to greet any other saxophonists who might still be arriving.

I suppose it's not surprising that Paul didn't recognize Ronnie Scott. He can only have seen his face in pictures and I don't think he's ever been to the club for the simple reason that he'd probably be mobbed if he went there. Being a Beatle can play havoc with your social life!

London

I was on the first ever live world-wide television programme, shown to four hundred million people in twenty-four countries!

There had been talk of a big TV link-up round the world for some time and at last the boys were chosen to represent the United Kingdom. What better message could there be in 1967 than "All You Need Is Love"? As usual, there was an enormous amount of organizing before what looked like a spontaneous party was arranged. Fortunately, the BBC and EMI did most of it this time.

My job was nice and simple, for once. All I had to do was pick up Jane from Cavendish Avenue and take her in the limousine round to the EMI studios at Abbey Road, where Paul and the boys had spent the day setting things up. Now I knew that my plain old business suit and shinny shoes wouldn't be the right things to wear at a psychedelic party like this, so I bought a bright orange shirt especially for the occasion. I tried not to look in the mirror when I put it on, hoping that it wouldn't be the most horrible piece of clothing on view to the world! I did rebel over one thing — my shoes were still shiny!

When I arrived at Cavendish Avenue, Jane took one look at my shirt and said, "Paul's left a shirt for you to wear, Alistair."

"I'm wearing one. I've even left my tie at home!"

"Oh no, that's not good enough. He said that he knew you'd dress in straight clothes and you wouldn't want to be in psychedelic gear, so he's bought a shirt specially for you to wear tonight."

Jane brought out a beautifully made silk shirt, with a multicolored pattern on it that looked as if it had been painted by Picasso with a pallet knife! I admitted defeat and went off to put it on.

The scene in the huge EMI studio was unbelievably glittering. You couldn't turn round without bumping into somebody famous! It must have been the most fantastic assembly of pop music personalities ever. In the middle of the kaleidoscope, setting the pattern, were the boys. They were terribly nervous, more than I've ever seen them before, particularly John. Well, the minutes were ticking away to something bigger than anyone ever tried to do before, so no wonder we were terrified. It's not every day that hundreds of millions of people are looking at the boys!

As I wandered round the party, I noticed that there were four sandwich boards stacked against the wall. You know, the sort of boards you see old men wearing around London with "Repent, the End of the World is Nigh" on one side and on the other "Eat at Mac's fish Restaurant'! Each of these boards had one side reading "All you Need is Love" and the other had the same message but in a different language. I was just idly inspecting them when some people from the office came up.

"Come on, Al, try one of these on!"

"Oh no, not me," I back-pedalled.

"Yes, you've got to. They suit your shirt!"

"Oh well, if you insist." At least a sandwich board might cover it up!

So there I was, wandering about like a turtle with this multi-lingual message on my multicolored back, while the boys sang their song to the world and we all trooped past the cameras for the chorus and the final shots. It was a superbly successful programme and it didn't stop there. We partied for most of the night!

When I saw the tapes later on, though, I noticed that all the other board carriers had been given full close-ups, while I'd just passed in front of the cameras. If you sneezed, you'd miss seeing me. In that shirt, that might be just as well!

London

At last the great day has come and the boys have released *Sergeant Pepper's Lonely Hearts Club Band* — or Pepper, as we know it. This is the biggest record they'll ever make, I think, the absolute spirit of all their music. It's certainly taken an age to record, so long that the weeks and the months have merged into each other for all of us. There must have been hundreds of hours of recording consigned to the waste bin and what's left has been polished to perfection. The effect of all this effort on the boys has been massive. I remember bumping into Ringo at the Speakeasy a few weeks ago and he was grey with fatigue, utterly shattered.

I see some of the critics and moralists have brought out their knife grinders again. It's the usual thing, I suppose, saying that the album's full of drug symbolism and that the Beatles are constant drug users, that sort of rubbish. Sure, everyone knows there are drugs on the pop music scene, but it's ridiculous to imagine that the boys must be stoned all the time. If anyone asks me about it, I ask them in return how they think the Beatles can be heavy drug users and still manage to do as much work as they get through: writing, recording, arranging, appearances, travel! They'd long ago have died of exhaustion if they'd done half of what some of their critics suggest they do.

Even the words on the album are up for inspection and dissection. "Four thousand holes in Blackburn, Lancashire" isn't a testimony to heroin injection in the northwest. John just read a newspaper report which said that Blackburn Council had sent out a guy to survey the local roads and he'd counted four thousand holes which needed filling in! So John added the bit about the Albert Hall and put the four thousand holes into "Day in the Life'. Terrible, isn't it? I'm sure these people would have made out that Shakespeare was a drug addict if they'd been left alone with *Twelfth Night* for half an hour!

As for "Lucy in the Sky with Diamonds', and the mystical significance of the letters LSD, John himself told me the answer to this one, before any of the critics even heard the song. One afternoon, Julian brought home from school a picture that he'd drawn.

"What's that? What have you drawn?" asked John.

"That's my girlfriend, Lucy, in the sky," came the reply.

"What are all those marks around her?"

"Those are diamonds."

End of myth. Sorry if it's not more exciting!

It's not just the boys who've been working themselves into the ground. The album cover for Pepper caused its own headaches. Originally it was going to be on an even grander scale, but after what seemed like dozens of suggestions the boys settled on the idea of featuring all those faces. They just loomed around and drew up a fantastic list of the people they wanted to be on the cover. Now you'll recognize the boys and the wax models of their younger selves from Madame Tussaud's, Marilyn Monroe, Diana Dors, Fred Astair, Bob Dylan, Marlon Brando, and Laurel and Hardy. You might even spot Shirley Temple, Max Miller and Karl Marx.

But would you know Issy Bonn, the singer who used to be popular about twenty years ago? Or Albert Stubbins? Who? Albert Stubbins played football for Liverpool years ago and his chief claim to fame was that when he moved to Anfield Liverpool paid out a record transfer fee for him!

Now, we couldn't use any of these people's faces until we'd found them or the executors of their wills and paid them a halfpenny each for the privilege! You can imagine what a nightmare that was for Wendy Hanson, who had to do the hunting! Still, she found them all in the end!

London

I wasn't around when Brian and George Martin first met; that was during my stay with Pye. I well remember the dreadful time that Brian had while he was trying to find a recording contract for the boys, though.

Brian was the finest record retailer in the North of England — perhaps in the whole country — and the record companies knew that he had a nose for a hit record. The trouble was that the Artiste and Repertoire men (the A & R men) were totally separate from the sales divisions of the companies and they didn't want to know about a group being touted by a man they considered to be a jumped-up record shop owner. Brian contemplated trying to put pressure on the companies by threatening to cancel his record orders with them, but at last he arranged an audition with Decca.

We all know now that Dick Rowe of Decca turned the boys down, which must have been the biggest mistake anyone made since I turned down two-and-a-half per cent of the Beatles! I don't hold it against Dick, though. At least he listened to what they had to offer and came to a rational business decision, even if it was the wrong one. Nobody else did as much until Syd Coleman put Brian in touch with George Martin at Parlophone. That was about when I left, when Brian was waiting for George Martin to return his call, and looking more and more miserable as the days went by.

Still, that's all history now. George is firmly established as what some people call the "Fifth Beatle', although few would recognize him in the street. George's great strength lies in the recording studio, where he has an uncanny ability to sense what the boys want even before they put it into words. Paul will say, "We want something in there," and hum a bar or two, and George will come up with just the right way of filling the space. It's as if he acts as a focus for their thoughts, analyzing and refining them into what they really want, with his incredible ability to interpret their wishes.

George has always known that the Beatles have immense talent, even though they were pretty crude in the beginning. His other great contribution has been never to use his superior musical knowledge to put the boys down. If one of the boys has an idea, George will always listen to it. The conversations go something like this:

"Why can't we do it like that, George?"

"Well, it's never been done, John."

"Why not, George?"

"Well, John, you aren't supposed to be able to do that."

"Why not, George?'

"All right, we'll try it."

In the end, George is willing to give any musical idea a try, and he never deliberately makes a mess of it to prove his point. Some producers would do that, but never George. A shared sense of humor helps, of course, and George can trade line for line with any of the boys. The relationship is simply a perfect piece of chemistry!

Let me give you just one example of George's ability to accept new ideas. We were up at Abbey Road and the recording wasn't going too well. John knew he wanted a certain sound but the trouble was that he didn't know what the sound was! It wasn't a musical sound that he wanted, but he couldn't quite pin it down. He kept disappearing from the studio and wandering around the offices. At last he came rushing in and yelled, "I've got it." He was carrying a short-wave radio that he'd found in one of the offices and he wanted the garbled sound that the radio made to be fed into the board. George didn't even raise an eyebrow; he just arranged for the radio to be recorded. I can't think of many producers who'd do that!

By the way, don't think that because the Beatles songs are credited to John and Paul as composers George and Ringo don't contribute. If you were there in the studio, you'd see that John and Paul are the driving force, but the other two don't just sit there and do as they're told. Ringo might made suggestions about the beat and George might have an idea for a different guitar riff. The whole business of recording is a partnership between John, Paul, George, Ringo and George Martin. George Harrison would be a major composer in popular music. I wish he'd compose more, but he does tend not to push himself forward much. I expect he will come to the front in his own good time.

Paul and John don't write together very much, not while I'm watching, anyway, but they can when the pressure's on. We were once absolutely desperate to put out a single, with EMI breathing down our necks and waving the recording contract at us. John just went round to Cavendish Avenue and sat down with Paul to write a single in cold blood. But that was quite unusual.

The boys aren't very interested in singles, these days. They always were more into albums. Another thing, if you look in the albums that the boys have made, you won't find their current singles in them. Brian and the boys have always thought that it's unfair on the fans to record a single and sell a few million, then release an album which contains two singles and their flip sides which the fans will already have. I think the American companies think they're crazy not to do that. Nothing but value for money from the boys!

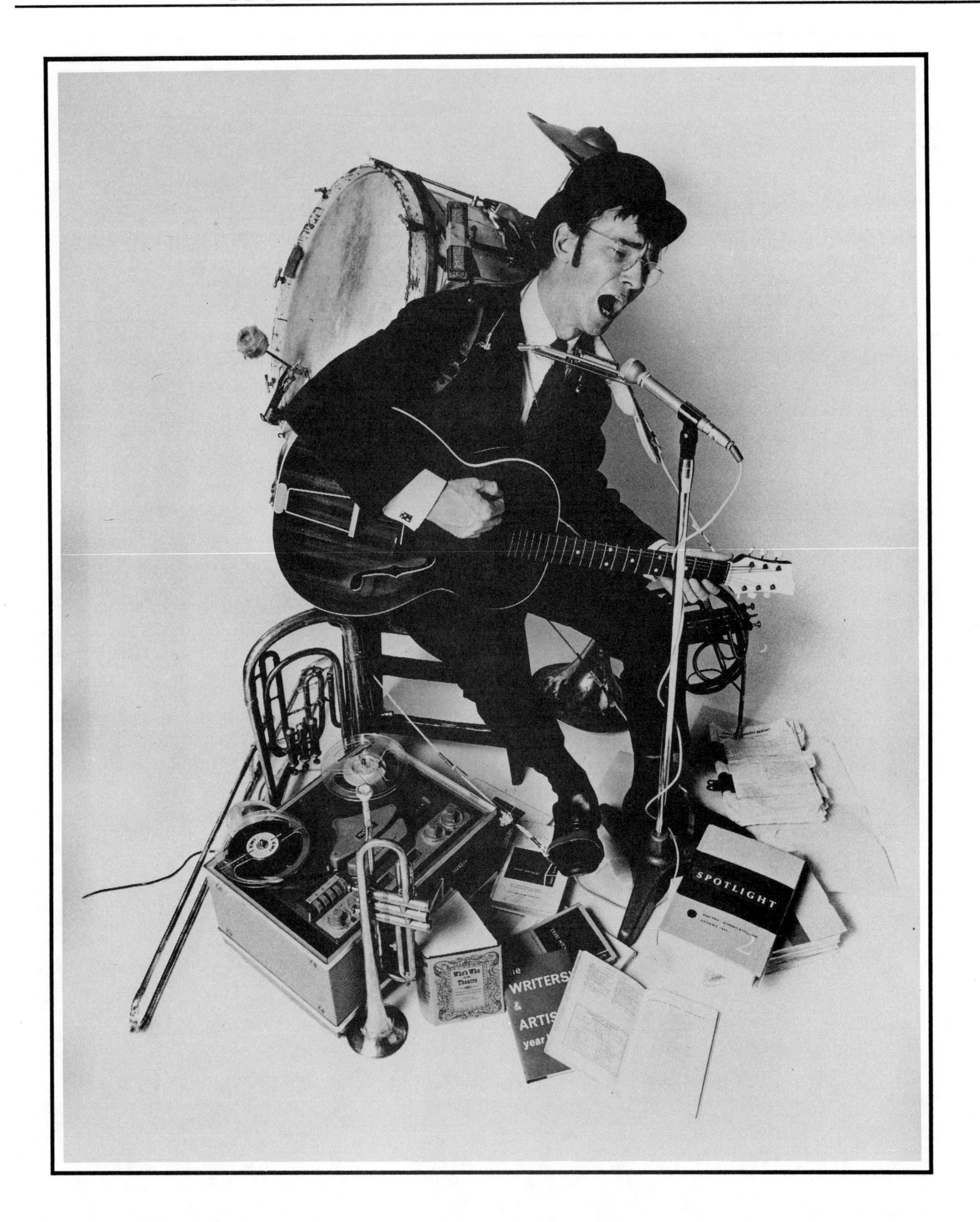

Alistair posing for the advertisement which Apple placed on the back of NME, April 1968. (Alistair Taylor)

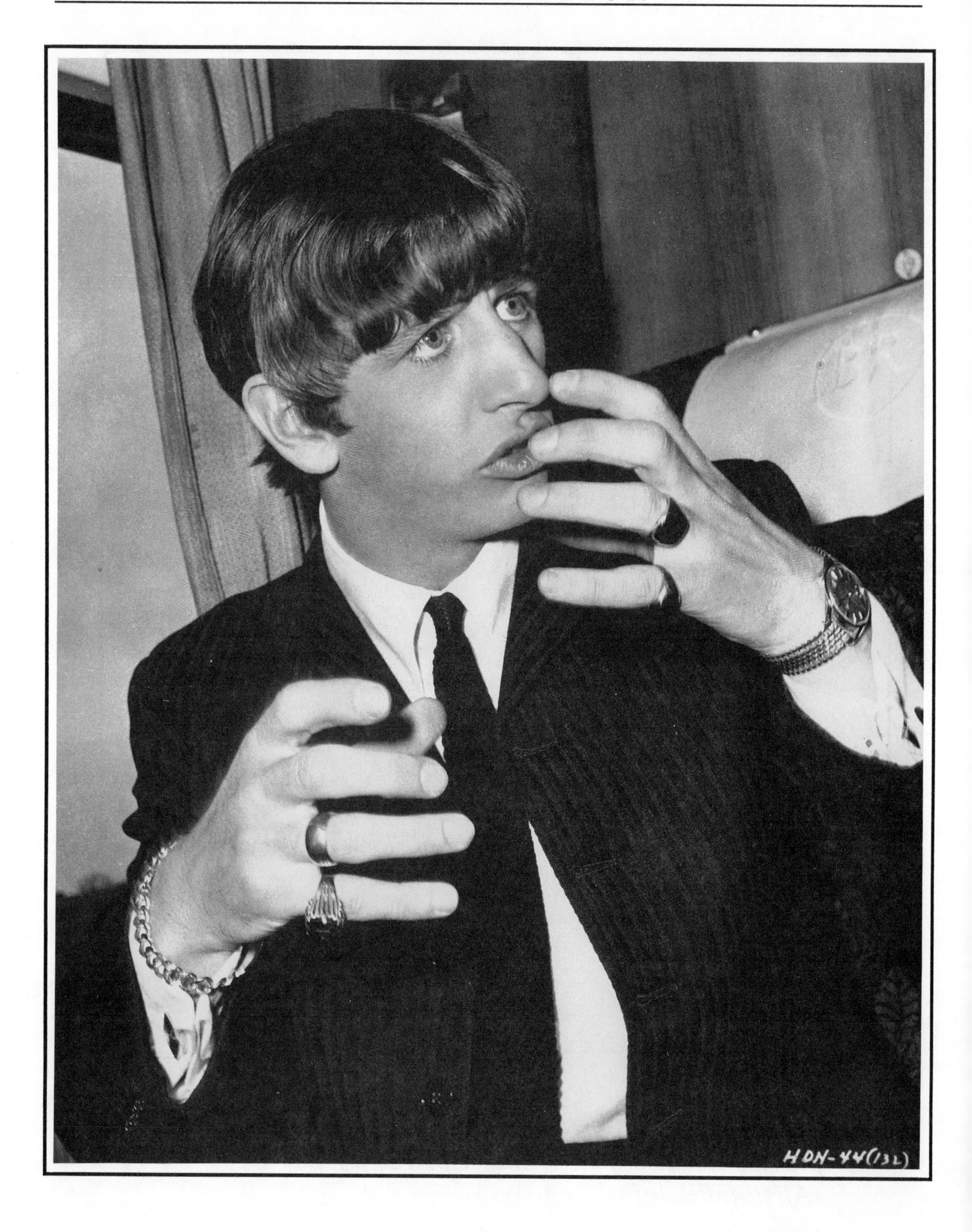
HDN-44(132)

Photo on this and preceding page from A HARD DAY'S NIGHT
(used courtesy of Walter Shenson)
Photo on following page from HELP!
(used courtesy of Walter Shenson)

H-2

9

CHAPTER

Heathrow

Magic Alex, the boys" Greek electronics expert, and I are heading to Athens, off for a few days in the sun looking for an island for the Beatles to buy.

We were all up at Abbey Road in the recording studio the other night. Alex Mardas was there, fiddling about with some new electronic creation, and we were all just chatting during a coffee break. Suddenly the boys started to talk about buying an island. "We're fed up with always living in this country. If it's not raining, the fans are chasing us all over the place. Harold Wilson's taxing us something rotten and on top of that we're always being told that Britain's going to the dogs and we're somehow to blame. Talk about 1967 being the Summer of Love! We want to buy an island, not here in Britain, but somewhere warm and away from the crowds."

That was about the sum of their feelings, and I can't say that I blame them. I didn't remind John that I bought Dorinish for him and he's hardly looked at the place since. It isn't that sort of windswept desolation that the Beatles are looking for.

Alex put down his screwdriver and, in his usual rather broken English, stuck in his oar. "Why don't you buy an island in Greece? They are very cheap there, almost given away. Very warm in winter and in summer."

Well, that was it. The idea grew in the boys" minds visibly, like a bamboo shoot. Within five minutes it was settled. Alex is to go and find some islands in Greece for the boys to look at and I'm to go along too, because I know the sort of things the Beatles like. We're to make a short list of likely places and then all the Beatles will come out with their families to combine island-hunting with a loony holiday in the sun. Can't be bad, especially as it means Alistair has two trips away from dirty old London.

London

In Athens Magic Alex and I met a Cretan solicitor friend of Alex's — his name's so unpronounceable that I'm not even going to try to spell it! We all had a meal together, then drove down to Piraeus and boarded an overnight ferry to Crete, where Alex's friend had a property lined up for me to see. "But the boys want an island," I protested. No matter, they insisted. I'd love the property, which was just the thing for the Beatles, especially since not many people come to Crete. Well, why not? It wouldn't do any harm to see the place.

Greek car ferries are amazing. There wasn't a restaurant or even a bar, simply some cabins (we booked one each) and a huge expanse of open wooden deck. It was so hot that I spent most of the night on deck, not wanting to go to bed in my stuffy little cabin with its odd-smelling bed. As dawn approached, the ferry's public address system crackled an announcement in Greek and began softly to play bouzouki music and there, seen dimly at first through a rapidly clearing mist, was my first sight of the hills of Crete.

Once off the ferry, we had to shift quickly. We had to drive along the entire island, take in a sight of this property, and then a night ferry trip back from the other end. If Athens had been hot, Crete was blisteringly equatorial. Although I was dressed only in thin jeans, a cotton shirt and open sandals, I could feel the sweat pouring off me as we jolted along mile after mile of these awful roads.

At about one o'clock I was beginning to feel very hungry and it was an hour since I'd seen any sign of civilization.

"Hey, Alex. When are we going to stop for something to eat? I'm starving."

A quick burst of Greek between Alex and his friend. "It OK, Alistair. It OK."

Suddenly we turned off the road, down a narrow track that led through a steep-sided ravine. Where on earth were we going? There wasn't a Wimpy bar in sight!

"We swim first, then we eat. Is OK?"

The track suddenly opened out on to the kind of beach you see photographed at five in the morning on Midsummer's Day and stuck in the travel agent's window. We all changed into our swimming trunks and started to run across that dazzling sand. It was so hot that we burnt the soles of our feet, so it was back to the car for sandals before cooling off in the Aegean.

It was so hot that we were bone-dry by the time we reached the car. Feeling a lot cooler after our swim, we drove on for about twenty minutes until Alex's friend turned off down another track which led to a tiny village in the hills. Sitting on the verandah of the local cafè and dressed in full Cretan costume were three grey-moustached old men — all smoking hookahs! Now there was a mind-blowing sight!

An unpleasant thought tickled my spine. Was this bandit country? I whispered to Alex, "Are we all right?"

"Is OK."

I had to settle for that and wait until Alex's friend came back, this time with all his family in tow!

"We have food in minute. Drink first."

That suited me, so we went off to the cafè and drank retsina for ten minutes until a lady came and led us up a side street to a sunny open patio of a brilliant white cottage. Spread out on tables was the most tempting feast imaginable; all sorts of salads, fish, omelettes and any amount of wine.

The three of us were ushered to the only three seats at the table and helped ourselves, while the rest of the village watched. Presently all of the villagers came up in turn to be introduced to me and to shake hands. I have never been made to feel so welcome anywhere — and I come from the North of England!

Time went by and I began to keep one eye on my watch — there was still a lot of driving to do. Should we offer to settle up? After all, they didn't look very prosperous, and we had been given a royal meal. I whispered something along these lines to Alex, but he said, "No, they will be very insulted if you offer to pay." All the same, it didn't seem right that I should be so singled out for attention. They'd never even met me before! These thoughts were running through my head when a tall, handsome guy in his late twenties came up and introduced himself as the son of the house. Small world indeed — he'd been trained as a doctor in London! Since his English was as good as mine, I asked him whether we ought to offer something in return for all the hospitality.

"Oh no," he laughed. "My family and friends will be very insulted if you offer to pay for your food. It is our custom here in Crete to look after any bona fide traveller. It has been so since Minos ruled the island three thousand years ago. Whatever you do, don't offer to pay!"

After long goodbyes we drove off to look at the property. It was useless to the Beatles and I suspect we'd all known it would be. Still, I had managed to get a feel for the customs of Greece, I suppose!

The car ferry from the other end of Crete took us back to Athens. We flew to Salonika and hired a boat to take us round the islands for a couple of days. Nothing seemed remotely suitable there, so we headed back to Athens, where Alex had discovered yet another promising piece of real estate. We drove out of Athens to a local village and took a fishing boat out ... to Paradise.

There's one big island of about eighty acres with four superb beaches and at least four other smaller islands surrounding it, all habitable. The main island has sixteen acres of olive groves, reckoned to produce the finest olives in the district. The village consists of half a dozen tall old Greek houses set on a gently curving bay which is filled with brightly colored high-prowed wooden fishing boats. It turns out that one family owns the island and all the business on it and they want to sell it, houses, boats, olive groves, the lot; £90,000 for the package.

This is a perfect setting for the Beatles. Think of it — a main island where they could build a recording studio and whatever else they wanted, and a small island each where they could take themselves off to if they fell out with each other. It makes financial sense too. There's a big olive oil company who buy the harvesting rights on the islands and would carry on the deal with us. I looked up the price of olives back in Athens and I reckon that the income from the olive groves will pay for the place in about seven years, then it will all be profit!

I couldn't wait to fly back to London to show the Beatles the pictures. Their reaction? They love it. All I have to do is arrange the finances and set up a holiday for us all to go and inspect the latest bit of potential British soil!

London

Well, we're just about to set off on our trip to show the Greek island to the Beatles, but what a time we've had trying to negotiate with Her Majesty's Government first! Your not allowed to take more than a few pounds in cash out of the country. That same sort of rule applies to spending money on property abroad. I didn't know anything about this law until I started to arrange the finance for buying this island.

It seems that you can't just take a sackful of pound notes out of the back of the car or write out a check. Oh no, you have to buy currency called property dollars from our government and pay with those.

We duly filled in all the forms and applied to buy £90,000-worth of property dollars. Back came the answer within a few days — a flat no.

Being born to argue, we all sat down with the solicitors and accountants and wrote a letter on four sides of paper detailing all the achievements of the Beatles, including the MBEs, and all the foreign currency they have earned for this country — much more than a mere £90,000. Also, this island isn't going to be a company project; it's a private purchase for the use of the Beatles as individuals. They call it something to buy with all their sixpences — sixpence being about all that is left over out of each pound taxed by the government! With fingers crossed, we sent off the letter and now we're waiting anxiously for the reply.

Much of this financial side of things is so much Greek to me. We truly miss Brian's influence here. I'm sure he'd be able to find a way round the problem, but he's not well at the moment. Besides, he considers the whole project a waste of time and he's virtually washed his hands of it. You may be wondering why we don't use some of the vast amount the Beatles earn overseas to buy the island. Again, I think we've got to thank Brian for setting an example of straight dealing and fair play to all of us and if that sounds like something out of a Boy Scouts" handbook, it's still the truth. NEMS always plays fair and pays up, just like Brian insisted when he used to lecture us in that narrow back office in Whitechapel all those years ago. I think the boys have taken on a lot of Brian's attitudes to business, almost without realizing it. Well, they haven't chosen to be tax exiles, have they?

Enough of this amateur city page analysis. The good news is that we're leaving for Greece tomorrow to take a cruise around the islands — and not in a fishing boat, either. Magic Alex has flown off in advance to hire a huge motor yacht with twelve cabins and all the luxury fittings to which I might find it very easy to become accustomed! We'll need most of the cabins to put up the party: Paul and Jane, John, Cynthia and Julian, George and Patti, Patti's sister, Ringo and Maureen, Big Mal Evans and his wife, Neil Aspinall and me. Tomorrow night we should all be relaxing at Alex's father's house in Athens, waiting to set sail.

The Aegean Sea

I'm not terribly good at writing on moving ships, especially as we seem to be in one of those patches of rough water between two islands, but I have an hour or two to spare as I sit on the deck of this magnificent motor cruiser. Such a lot has happened out here, I'd better do the decent thing and start at the beginning.

When we flew out, John suddenly said to me, "Alistair, where's Lesley?"

"At home, John."

"Why isn't she with us? Everyone else is."

"I wouldn't dream of just bringing her along on a trip like this," I replied.

That wasn't enough for John. "Look," he insisted, "when we arrive in Athens, get on the phone to her straightaway and tell her she's to come out here and have a holiday with us!"

I agreed to try, but I quietly let the matter drop. Lesley isn't keen to come abroad on a plane with me, let alone on her own. She's happiest at home, bless her.

Magic Alex was there to greet us at Athens airport as we stepped down on to the baking hot tarmac. We slipped quietly into Athens, quite differently from our usual arrivals in foreign cities.

It was only when we were all fed and watered that Alex broke some inconvenient news to us. The super millionaire's motor yacht that we were due to hire the next day had been caught in one of those fierce storms that blow up at this time of the year around Crete. This had delayed its return to Athens for refit and so the whole trip was going to be running several days late. The bottom line was that we were all going to have to stay in Athens for a few more days while the yacht was returned to its accustomed magnificence. Fine, we said. There are worse places to be delayed, you know, and the boys have been delayed in enough of them to know when they're on to a good thing!

Alex had set up some entertainment for us so that we wouldn't be bored. Unfortunately, he also seemed to have told our timetable to the Greek tourist people or somebody, because wherever we went there were crowds of people following us. Once, on a trip to a hill village, we came round a corner of the peaceful road only to find hundreds of photographers clicking away at us. Greek Beatle fans are better behaved than some English ones, though, and after a while they backed off a bit and let us have some peace.

I think they were too polite to thrust themselves at us and their hospitality at last won us over. We even ended up dancing like Zorba the Greek with our arms round each other's shoulders, while the village band played their bouzoukis to us. Quite a change from the Tower Ballroom! As for Alex, we forgave hm for leaking the news of our trip to the press without telling us; after all, he's done a lot for us, both in London and in Greece.

The crowds were thickest when we went shopping one morning in the main square of Athens. Several hundred people were quietly following us around, generally keeping their distance, but making Neil, Mal and me rather edgy. The Beatles could never have gone shopping openly in Birmingham or Glasgow and I suppose the three of us felt like tourists who are told that the lions almost never eat anyone!

So there we were, doing the rounds of the local stores, when we passed a music shop. The front window was festooned with all sorts of guitars: Gibsons, Fenders, Rickenbackers, all just like any music store in London or New York. John, however, spotted something new and darted straight in through the door, followed by the rest of us. The shopkeeper was standing behind the counter and his floppy moustache fairly stiffened when he saw who was coming in.

"Ah, the Beatles! Welcome to my little shop. What can I do for you? Would you like to see this beautiful new guitar — a Les Paul? Or perhaps this superb Gibson?"

"No thanks," said John. "I can get one of those at home. I want to buy one of these," and he picked up a humble-looking bouzouki. The shopkeeper just couldn't believe that John wasn't interested in any of his expensive electric guitars and he looked at the bouzouki as if he was ashamed of his native instrument. I think he should listen to the next few Beatles records — he'll probably hear that bouzouki being played!

The next shop was a jeweller's. Here was another businessman who could hardly believe what he was seeing when these wealthy young men walked through his front door (not us — the boys!). Within thirty seconds he'd pulled out all his most expensive display trays and sent his assistant to open the safe. He was bargaining away nineteen to the dozen with everyone ... well, almost everyone!

Every few minutes of this trip, I'd been doing a kind of mental sweep search, checking that all the boys and their families were safe and in sight. With a lurch in my stomach, I realized that the Beatle you'd expect to be in his element in a jeweller's shop was missing!

"Mal," I whispered, "have you seen Ringo?"

"No."

"Neil, have you seen Ringo?"

"God, no."

I looked around. Ringo couldn't be anywhere in the shop, not even on his hands and knees behind the counter. Outside, there was half of Athens staring through the shop window. Where on earth was he? Was he being mobbed somewhere? Or could he have been kidnapped? Oh, a true coward can really let his imagination go in a situation like that!

Neil, Mal and I agreed to split up and search different parts of the square. Five minutes later we pushed our way through the crowd and met outside the jeweller's shop again. None of us had seen any sign of Ringo. It was ten minutes since he'd last been seen, not a long time to lose sight of an ordinary friend, but long enough for a missing Beatle to become a major worry!

"Let's try inside the other shops," I suggested in desperation. "I know there's no crowd in front of any of them, so I don't think he can be inside, but someone might have seen him."

It was better than doing nothing, so all three of us eased our way back through the crowd and slipped into the shoe shop next door. And there, totally undisturbed, sitting on a chair and trying on a pair of sandals, was Ringo! He was even trying his hand at bartering in Liverpudlian Greek!

"How did you manage to get here?" I asked.

"What's the panic?" Ringo asked.

"There's about five thousand people out there, you know! What are you doing?"

"Oh, I didn't fancy buying any jewelry," he replied, casually walking around the shop to test the fit. "I decided I wanted some sandals for the trip. So I've been in here trying on a few pairs."

I suppose I worry unnecessarily. Ringo's got a lot of basic common sense. How he goes around in public without people recognizing him is beyond me — especially when I look at his face! Is there anyone on earth who looks exactly like Ringo? Yet he was sitting there without anyone realizing who he was!

Later on we all went out for the evening to one of the villages in the hills. We pulled up in the main square and walked over to the taverna. It was the usual Greek idea of a pub: a whitewashed building with tables and chairs set out in front, each covered by a straw shade. From inside came the sound of Greek bouzouki music — muzak, really, but it sounds so much better played on bouzoukis — wafting over the square. A timeless traditional scene, I thought — until the Beatles showed up.

About one minute after we all sat down, the gentle bouzouki music was cut off. A thump and a scratching noise came over the loudspeaker as a new record was put on. More bouzoukis? No. The whole village suddenly resounded to "Can't Buy Me Love" at full volume! The proprietor of the taverna came out with a big grin on his face. "Welcome to the Beatles!" If we went to the moon to get a little peace and quiet, a little green man with a television aerial on his head would pop out of the nearest crater holding a Beatles record in his tentacle!

So here we all are at last on this cruiser. It ain't half a change from the New Brighton ferry. There's a captain, his crew and two stewards, all of whom are here only to serve our every whim. We slipped out from Piraeus a few hours ago and are making our way to our dream island. We'll probably look at one or two others as well, but I'm saving the big one till the end!

Now I'm sitting here sipping my drink, flicking the odd insect away and listening to George gently playing the ukelele from somewhere forward.

Over the Alps

I'm on board a plane this time, flying back to London with instructions to push through the purchase of the island as quickly as possible!

That first night on board the yacht was dreadfully hot and after an hour or so of tossing and turning and fitfully dozing I woke up and decided that I'd never get any sleep down in my stuffy cabin. Why not sleep on deck, I thought. Quietly opening the cabin door so as not to disturb anyone, I tiptoed barefoot down the passage and crept up the stairs on to the deck. Outside, I could see a glorious full moon which I was admiring (and not looking where I was going) when I went sprawling over something soft lying on the deck. As I staggered against the rail to stop myself falling overboard, Paul's voice came sleepily up.

"Who the hell's that? What are you doing? God, it's hot."

"Sorry, Paul. It's me, Alistair. I didn't realize you were up here."

Jane's voice wafted up from the same place: "Most of us are up here. It's just too hot to sleep down there in the cabins."

And so they were. Instead of being the first with the marvellous idea of sleeping out on the deck, I was just about the last. So much for Alistair being clever! One thing I did, though, was to hang a towel over the rail of the cruiser which would face the sun. This would prevent me from being badly burned if I slept through the dawn, and I saw that most of the people asleep on deck had done the same thing. Alex had told me that that was the thing to do if I wanted to avoid looking like a lobster the next day. Poor old Mal. No one had told him about this neat trick, so he woke up the next day absolutely raw and red with sunburn! Where the horizontal cross-pieces of the rail had cast shadows on him, he had a few white strips of unscorched flesh, but the rest of him was brick-red. Much sloshing of sun tan lotion has made him look less like a big red tomato, but when I left he was still wincing every time he put on a shirt!

We had a marvellous cruise. The sun beat down for most of the days and nearly all the time the surface of the sea was glassy calm. All the same, there's no escaping from Beatle fans. The "jungle drums" that seem to tell the fans in Britain where the boys are going to be even before they decide to go there are just as efficient in Greece. Once we sailed up to a kind of natural canal through some rocks between two islands, which was spanned by a lifting bridge. As we chugged slowly up to the raised bridge, we saw thousands of the local people on either side, waving, shouting greetings and brandishing Beatles records. So much for getting away from it all into the wide blue yonder of the Aegean! We just waved back and shouted a few polite things in Greek, which probably made their day!

Still, these were small interruptions compared to the long days of peace we spent. The crew looked after us like royalty. Nothing was too much trouble for them and sometimes they seemed to be doing what we wanted even before we asked. On about the second day out from Piraeus, we stopped and lowered the swimming ladder into the water. Everybody changed and plunged into the warm sea for half an hour's splashing about the yacht. Very refreshing, too. As we climbed back up the side, a steward stood there holding a fresh towel for each of us, although in that heat we were just about dry almost before we reached the top of the ladder.

As John came to the top and took his towel, he turned to the rest of us who were milling about on the deck selecting places to sunbathe.

"Do you know, I always remember when I was a kid and I used to go swimming at the baths I always came home and had some porridge. I don't know why, but ever since I always think of porridge when I'm drying off after a swim!"

Fifteen minutes later, a beaming steward came out to where we were all lying sprawled in the baking sun. He was holding a large saucepan and following him was another steward with a tray of bowls and spoons, looking just as pleased with himself. The stewards were bringing us some steaming hot porridge! God knows why or how they managed to find porridge oats in their store room in the middle of the Aegean, but they'd come up with the genuine article!

Everybody roared with laughter, especially John, who took his plate of porridge and laid into it. Soon we were all spooning down hot porridge in the ninety-degree heat. We couldn't insult the stewards and cook, could we? We even scraped out the pan!

Later on, we dropped anchor in another of those hill-fringed bays and sent Alex on to the shore in one of the motor boats to buy as many pads of paper and colored pencils as he could lay his hands on. He came back laden with coloring books and with twenty sets of pretty crayons, so we decided to have a doodling competition to find who could design the most beautiful doodle. Everyone sat down with a pencil and a pad and for a few minutes there was total silence, for once. After a while, we all offered our results for the rest to judge and analyze. Most people had done various sorts of psychedelic doodles with bubbles and curls like the patterns made by the turning of an oil-wheel. One or two had done weird faces of animals. But I was the only one out of the whole of the party who'd doodled in straight lines! All my doodles were zigzags and squares, with hardly a curve in sight!

"All our corners are round, but all yours are sharp," laughed John. "Why do you doodle like that?"

"God knows," I said.

John spent quite a long time studying my pathetic doodles, trying to work out why I was the odd doodler out, but he couldn't come up with any answer better than, "It must have been something in your childhood, Alistair'! I suppose it must. It didn't seem that important to me, but every so often John would look at me as if to say, "Sharp corners ... ah ha!" We used up all the pads and pencils, just doodling and drawing and passing the time in a relaxed and mindless way, for once.

For me, though, the golden moment of the whole trip came one moonlit evening. Some of us (John, George, Mal and me, I think) were sitting out on the deck just above the bows of the yacht, watching a glorious blood orange Greek moon. The captain was holding the yacht on a course directly along the beam of light that the moon threw on to the slightly rippled surface of the sea. It seemed as if we were sailing through the far heavens to the moon, never seeming to come any closer, but knowing that if the night was long enough we might, we just might, sail the whole distance and reach harbor on one of the seas of the moon itself. Anything seemed possible to us as we sat there, totally relaxed.

John, Mal and I had been chanting Hare Krishna while George gently picked out the notes on his ukelele, but at last we had stopped, utterly at peace with the world, sitting there with legs crossed in the lotus position and staring along the shiny column of the moonbeam. We must have been sitting there for nearly two hours, with the rush and push of Beatlemania utterly forgotten in this newfound peace and tranquillity.

At last I broke the silence. "Just look at that moon."

John's laconic voice spoke from beside me. "Well spotted, Alistair!"

Now they won't let it go. Whenever I point out anything to them, someone says, "Well spotted, Alistair!"

So on we sailed for day after sunlit day, sometimes putting into the lesser islands which I'd lined up for the boys to see. They loved them, but I kept saying. "Wait, just hold on. Just enjoy the sail. Don't do anything until you've seen the really tremendous one!"

At last the anchor chain rattled down into the blue waters of the olive island's bay and our yacht lay there among the brightly painted local fishing boats like a Rolls-Royce in a rickshaw park.

"Yeow! This can't be true!" came the yell from everybody as they surveyed the bay, taking in the main island and the little surrounding islets, the olive groves, the fishing fleet, the white-painted old Greek houses scattered along the waterfront. In a few seconds, both motor boats were launched and a whooping party of Beatles was heading at full speed towards the shore. All day they explored the place, setting off for the other little islands and meeting each other to compare notes, telling each other where the main house could be, discussing where they wanted the recording studios to be built, joking about who could live on which island, all totally in love with the place.

By the end of that day, yesterday, they'd come to their decision. "Go back straight away, Alistair, and start arranging for the property dollars. £90,000 is a bargain price for this place!"

So that's it. My job in Greece is over now that I've found the island and guided the Beatles to it. Now I can see a busy time ahead as I catch up with all the work that's bound to have piled up in the office and carry on with our argument about the property bonds with the government. It all depends on whether we're allowed to buy them.

This is going to be the Fixit of all time if it comes off. In a way, I'm glad that the rest of them have decided to stay out in Greece for another week. I'll need all my concentration in London, and it'll be a relief not to be diverted by any other little odd jobs for a week or so.

Well, we're coming in to land at Heathrow, so I'll close this. Tomorrow I'll see what the government says. Oh, I do hope they see sense and let us go ahead and buy the island in Paradise!

London

That's my holiday in the Aegean finished. When I went into the office, I found the reply to our letter asking the government to reconsider their refusal to sell us property dollars. I opened it with some trembling, because if they refused to let us take the money out of the country, then the whole project was a dead duck anyway.

The letter, signed by James Callaghan, sounded quite promising. Yes, we could buy the £90,000-worth of property dollars in recognition of the services rendered to the country by the Beatles. Great, I thought. Of course, there was a sting in the tail in the form of a final paragraph which stated that as this was the absolute limit they didn't know how we were going to furnish the place. Thank you very much. We only want to build a studio and a housing complex and a house on each of four outlying islands and buy boats for getting around and so on and so on!

Still, we don't give up easily. Setting the accountants and solicitors to carry on with the negotiations in more detail, I went ahead and bought £90,000-worth of property dollars, which took a very large slice out of our current funds.

Now I'm no financial wizard. After all, I'm still quite skinny even after all these years with the Beatles! Still, as far as I can tell, this is what happens. Property dollars are bought at a premium of so much per cent and it turned out that the day after I bought ours the premium rose by about seven per cent. I'm told that this means that we've made a paper profit already! Suits me.

London

The Beatles came back from their holiday in Greece, still full of excitement about the place,still keen to build their houses and studio on it. When I told them about Mr Callaghan's letter that said we could only have the bare £90-000-worth of property dollars, they were a bit fed up. I told them that we were only just starting negotiations; they must be patient, and I hoped we'd be able to buy enough dollars to make the island into the earthly paradise we wanted. So on I went, keeping in touch with the accountants and solicitors, concocting letters begging to be allowed more money, and generally making some headway.

The other day, Neil had some news for me: "Forget the Greek island."

"What did you say?" I gasped.

"Forget the Greek island."

"You're joking," I snorted. "I've spent bloody weeks on this project! What's the matter? Have they thought of something else?"

"No, but frankly they're so pissed off with all the aggro involved in buying it that they've said that the government can stick their money and they'll think of something else. They don't want to know."

I could hardly believe this. After all, the negotiations with the government weren't going that badly. At least we were still talking about it.

"Right," I insisted, "I'm not doing a thing for another week."

Neil laughed. "Good thinking. You know what they're like."

Over the next few days I spoke to each of the boys in private and put it straight to them. Once the project was cancelled, that would be it. They couldn't just change their minds again. At last they had another meeting and were absolutely unanimous. They'd work out something else.

This left us with £90,000-worth of property dollars which were now worth more than when I'd bought them, since the premium on buying them had gone up. I decided to have just one more meeting with all of them, Neil included. This was the final chance to say yes.

"Now, are all of you absolutely certain you don't want this island? In a few minutes, I'm going back to my office, I'm going to pick up the phone and I am selling the property dollars back to the government."

There was no doubt or hesitation at all. Paul even asked me if I wanted it in writing! All right.

Downstairs I went to my office and I rang the accountants, telling them to sell the property dollars.

"Alistair, hang on," came the reply. "You know what the boys are like."

"Sell," I demanded. "Now. This morning. No messing."

"What's the hurry?"

"We stand to make about six or seven per cent of £90,000 out of this government, that's the hurry. Sell them now."

So within a quarter of an hour the dollars were back in the government's hands at the new increased premium and we were that much better off. Ah well, it's an ill wind that blows no one any good, but I miss the thought of spending holidays on that beautiful island!

London

We've recovered from the disappointment about the Greek island. Things are very relaxed at the moment, actually. I spent a good part of today lying on the floor doodling?

John had asked me to come out to Kenwood to go through some papers with him, so out I went, ready for a heavy business session. When I arrived, I found John and Julian in the kitchen, lying on their stomachs.

"Hi there, Al!" shouted John. "Julian and I are having a drawing session. Grab some paper and one of those pencils over there and come join us."

There was no chance of doing any paperwork while John was in that mood, so I lay down on the floor and joined in the doodling with John and Julian, two grown men and a little boy — or perhaps three little boys really! Despite all John's efforts to understand them, I'm still doing square drawings!

10
CHAPTER

London

This has been a hell of a weekend for Alistair.

Late on Saturday afternoon, Brian phoned with a little job for me. "Alistair, two guitarists are coming over from the States tomorrow morning to discuss some recording contracts with me. I've booked them into a hotel, but I won't be able to meet them at Heathrow. Could you go along and make contact with them, please? It's really only a matter of greeting them and putting them into a taxi."

"Sure, Brian. When does their flight arrive?"

"Six o'clock."

"In the morning?"

"Yes. Sorry it's so early, but it's the best I can do. I'd go myself, but I'm supposed to be meeting people in a club tonight and I think we'll be up all night."

"All right, Brian. I'll be there."

"Thank you, Alistair. All the details are in my office. All the visas and work permits should have been arranged, and I wired them some money for the trip."

I set the alarm for five o'clock on Sunday morning, intending to be out of bed for only just long enough to put the Americans into a taxi. With luck, I could be back under the blankets before seven-thirty. It took quite an effort to pull myself out of bed so early, but I threw on an old roll-neck sweater and some slacks, downed a cup of scalding coffee and set out, bleary and unshaven, for the airport.

Heathrow in the early hours of a Sunday morning is not the hub of the universe. The arrivals lounge was empty except for two West Indian cleaners gloomily hovering cigarette ash off the carpet. Not one of the shops was open yet and the whole place felt stale and empty. The arrivals board showed that the flight I was meeting had already landed, so I wandered over to the exit door of Immigration.

Suddenly the arrivals lounge came alive as a stream of people filtered through, a trickle at first, then a surge, like water from an unblocked gutter. Now where are my two Americans, I thought, as I held up my NEMS placard on the tip of my umbrella (one day I'll hold up a "Beatles" placard and see what happens!). I stood there like a lemon while all the crowd went past, taking no notice of me. None of them even looked like an American guitarist.

Wrong flight, I thought. Now what happens? Before I had a chance to do anything, the public address system crackled into life. "Will the representative of NEMS Enterprises come to the Information desk, please?"

Sure enough, there was trouble. The Americans didn't have proper entry visas and work permits, they'd spent all their money before setting off, and the result was that Immigration weren't letting them into the country. They were stuck in the stateless limbo of the airport like displaced persons, and they didn't like it at all. This time, nothing I could do moved the officials one inch. I explained who NEMS Enterprises represents. No go. I showed them the file which I'd taken from Brian's office. No go. I tried appeals to their sympathy, suggestions of a mistake on their part (this was a mistake of mine!) and even a touch of arrogant Beatlepower. No go. How the hell had these characters left the States with their papers in such a mess?

This was a dead end that no Fixit could break through. Doubtless Immigration would have let in the Beatles themselves in similar circumstances; they're usually the image of helpfulness to us. What they wouldn't do was extend the same tolerance to just any unknown acquaintances of NEMS. The best they could offer was to send these two to Paris and keep them there until we could work something out. Very useful.

By the time I'd been shunted from office to office, the morning had passed into that particular web of timelessness which all airports spin around themselves. When I finally admitted defeat, it was a shock to look up at the clock and see that it was past eleven o'clock.

Only one option was left. The last shot in the locker, the red panic button — call Brian and admit failure. This was a double blow to my pride, because I've never before had to say that I can't fix something. Still, I had managed to prevent the guitarists being shipped back across the Atlantic on the first plane — that was something. I didn't know how Brian would take an admittance of defeat, and I felt very miserable as I stood at the phone in my crumpled roll neck and sprouting stubble.

"Wait there. I'm on my way." The phone went dead. Oh well, let Brian have a go at getting these two into the country. He'll do no better than I did.

On the stroke of noon Brian swept into the office where I was waiting with the Americans. He had obviously only just arrived home after his night out when I called, but he was immaculate as ever, dressed in sports jacket and knife-edged slacks. I felt even scruffier.

Like a sergeant-major inspecting a new recruit, Brian took one look at me and said,'I'll talk to you later." He then disappeared into an inner office with the Immigration people and the Americans.

Twenty minutes later, I was feeling like the original seven-stone weakling as Brian loaded the guitarists into a taxi and told the driver the name of their hotel. How he got them into the country I just don't know, but there must be weapons in the Beatlepower armory even I have never seen.

Brian turned to me with a look of tightly controlled anger on his face such as I haven't seen since I double-booked the Beatles back in 1962. "Just look at you; you're a disgrace to the business, coming to an airport dressed like that — and not even shaven!"

I considered my fraying sweater and scraped a hand over my chin. "There wasn't anybody here to notice at six this morning, Brian. You led me to think it wouldn't take five minutes to meet them, so I didn't dress up. Do you realize I've spent five hours trying to get them into the country?"

"I don't care what time it was. When you represent me and the Beatles, you dress properly. We must maintain the highest standards at all times. Don't you remember the lecture I gave the Beatles when they signed the contract? The same applies to you. As for this ridiculous business, why can't anybody be trusted to carry out a simple task? Nobody in this company can do anything at all. It's time to set it right."

I didn't answer this one. If somebody had made a mess of the paperwork, it wasn't me, and even Brian would realize that when he calmed down. But inside I was seething with anger at his boss-to-office-boy tone.

Brian thought for a moment, then strode over to a row of pay telephones. "Do you have any sixpences?" I came up with a handful and, stepping to the phone, he lifted the receiver. I wasn't sure whether my presence was still required, so I stayed close by, wondering what was going to happen.

Brian dialled a number and when the call was answered he just said, "Good morning. This is Brian speaking, just to let you know you're fired."

He put the receiver down, lifted it again and went through the same process until, by my reckoning, he'd sacked all of the directors of NEMS except Clive Epstein. Each of them had the same message, delivered in unemotional and controlled tones: "...just to let you know you're fired." The whole business took less than ten minutes. While I stood aghast. he was cutting NEMS to shreds, all because of a mix-up over two guitarists who probably deserved to sink without a trace anyway!

As Brian put down the phone, I tackled him. "I suppose that doesn't apply to me?"

"Yes, you're fired too," he hissed.

Just what I wanted to hear after six fruitless Sunday hours jumping to my master's voice! "Good, because I don't want to stay. I've been up since the small hours working for you and if you think you can find anyone who could do the job better, you're welcome to try. I've had enough! You can stick your job! I'll be in tomorrow morning to clear my desk."

"Alistair, come back!" Brian shouted. "Let's talk!" But I was already on my way home and I didn't turn back.

I left the airport with a strange feeling of relief. Brian has occasionally held the threat of the sack over me when he's been under pressure, but he must have known that I don't need that sort of motivation. Now that the moment had finally come, though, I was glad to be a free agent again. The travel, the cars, the entertainment allowances, they would all have to go, but at least I wouldn't be expected to live a double-time life, weekends and holidays included. It was with a light heart that I made my way back to the flat and ate a late Sunday lunch.

In the middle of the afternoon, the phone rang. I put down my coffee, turned the stereo down a fraction and picked up the receiver. Brian.

"Alistair, can we discuss your leaving the business, please?"

"I don't see that there's anything to discuss," I replied with equal calm.

"Well, can you come over and talk with me, please?"

"No, I can't. Sorry."

"May I come to see you, or we could meet somewhere else, if you like?"

"No, Brian. I don't work for you any more. I'll come into the office tomorrow morning to clear my desk and that's it." I put the receiver down on a very anxious and overwrought Brian. I had absolutely no intention of going back to work for him.

This morning I went into the office after a military-close shave, with a crease in my trousers you could have cut cheese with. What sort of job might an ex-manager of the Beatles be offered at the Labour Exchange? I was wondering.

The personal contents of my desk were safely packed into my briefcase when the door of the office opened and there was Brian, very crestfallen. Would I come back, please? Once again I refused, but this time Brian put it straight. I never knew I meant so much to him! He waxed lyrical about all I'd done for the Beatles and how no one else could have managed all the "fixing" so well. I blush to write it (well, not really!). Finally he asked me once again to consider coming back.

Of course I gave in. I really can't resist flattery, especially if it's true! Besides, there's a big wide world out there which might not yet be ready for unemployed ex-Beatles managers and I'm not ready to write my memoirs yet!

There was one condition. "Don't you dare ever to do anything like that to me again, Brian."

"Of course not, Alistair."

Only one other point remained. "What are you going to do about the others? You and I can't run the business alone, can we? You did sack just about the entire board of directors yesterday!"

"I know, but I didn't mean it. It was in a bad temper, that's all."

I left Brian alone with the telephone and his address-book. Sometimes a man needs his privacy.

London

I've moved my home. No, Lesley and I are still in our flat, but I've moved into different offices for a while. Some time ago, Brian took a private office here at Hille House, off Albemarle Street, so that he could work in peace away from everybody else. Lately, though, he's been working more and more from his own house in Chapel Street, where he invited me recently.

"Right, Alistair," he said, "I want you to concentrate much more on the boys and to make looking after them your main concern from now on. I think you should also move into my office at Hille House."

I don't mind the move at all, but I sometimes wonder whether it's a good idea for Brian to be so isolated from the rest of the organization. I like the Hille House office very much; in fact, I've used it quite a lot already and making it into my own place has been fun. For a start it's peaceful; below us is an expensive office furniture showroom and it just doesn't look like a Beatles building. That means that the fans don't hassle us when we're there. Really, I have very few visitors apart from the boys and their families and that means that Wendy Hanson and I can get through much more work than we used to be able to. A visit from a Beatle now helps to break the routine!

When Cynthia brings in little Julian, we always go through the same ritual. My office is a palatial affair with a huge table, at the end of a long corridor which leads from Wendy's reception office. When his mum brings Julian to see us, Wendy always gives be a buzz on the intercom and if I'm free I come out of my office into the corridor. As soon as Julian sees me, he gives a great yell of delight and pounds up the corridor as fast as his little legs will propel him. Then he dives at my legs and brings me down in a crunching rugby tackle! I always fall to my knees with a great crash and pretend to be lying there injured and in pain. Great fun! If I'm busy on the phone, Wendy has to keep Julian amused in the reception office until I can come out to be charged at. That's me, just a punch-bag!

Over the Atlantic!

I'm just coming back from a very unexpected trip to California with Cream, of all people.

It's a long story, and a rather odd one, in some ways. NEMS Enterprises merged with Robert Stigwood group a few months ago. Cream and the Bee Gees are two of Stigwood's acts that I've got to know a bit recently, but Brian hasn't been involving himself very much in anything but the Beatles since the merger. Even then he hasn't been into the office very often, but has preferred to work at home, cutting himself off from the daily life of the organization. This has meant that Robert Stigwood, as co-Managing Director, has been the man more at the centre of affairs.

Last Friday, I bumped into Robert walking down the corridor with Bob Masters, who does for him all that I do for Brian.

"How are the arrangements going for Cream's US tour?" I asked.

"They're going off to San Francisco on the twelve-thirty Pan-Am flight on Sunday, aren't they?" I was really just checking the details, because I'd arranged the air bookings, this being Cream's first US tour.

"Fine, Alistair," replied Bob.

"No problem about getting the US work permits, then?"

There was a horrible silence. "Work permits? What do you mean, work permits?" asked Bob, looking apprehensive.

"Did you arrange H2 visas, the ones that allow them to work while they're over there?"

"I don't know what you're talking about. I've got visas."

"Yes, but are they H2 work visas?" I pressed.

"No, I've got ordinary visitors visas," he admitted.

Robert Stigwood was furious. "You tell me then," he said to me. "What do we do now?"

"There's nothing you can do at this hour on a Friday afternoon. These things take ages to come through from the States. There's no use even starting to go through the usual channels now, less than forty-eight hours before you need the visas."

Utter crisis erupted. I wandered off back to my office. I've really nothing to do with the Stigwood acts, so I was content to let them sort it out for themselves. I should have known better.

Shortly afterwards, Robert Stigwood walked in. "Look, Alistair, can you help us?"

"I'll do my best, but I don't think there's much I can do."

"I'm really worried about this," he continued. "If this has gone wrong at this end, who knows what might be wrong at the other end? Can you possibly go out to San Francisco with Cream?"

"Robert, I would love a trip, but I really work for Brian. I don't want to be rude to you, but I must have his permission to go."

"Don't worry about that. I'll contact Brian. You just start to sort out this mess."

I rang the United States" Embassy, but they just told me that there was nothing doing; their visa section was closed for the weekend. I used a few names which I thought might be useful and made a few suggestions, but there was no chance.

"Is there anybody there tomorrow?" I asked.

"There is the Saturday duty officer," came the reply. "He won't be able to help you, though. We'd love to do something for you, but we just don't see what we can do."

If all else fails, go to the man at the top. I rang the Ambassador's residence and spoke to his assistant, who was equally gloomy but promised to call back. As long as they're still talking, I thought, we're in with a shout. At last the call came: if I would ring them on Saturday morning, they'd try to arrange something.

Robert can't have been too pleased at the lack of progress, but he took it well enough when I suggested that Cream should fly out on visitors visas and then we'd try to sort it out in the States. Meanwhile, I contacted Eric Clapton, Jack Bruce and Ginger Baker and told them that there might be a hitch. It seemed that I'd done everything I could, but Robert still couldn't find Brian. Without Brian's permission there was no way I was going to go.

On Saturday there was still no news from Brian. Robert was still assuring me that it would be fine for me to go and I was assuring him that I wouldn't go without talking to Brian first. There was better news at the Embassy. They'd pulled a few strings and promised that they could help me if I went to the Embassy at half-past ten on Sunday morning. What was more, Cream themselves didn't have to turn up in person to collect the visas; the Americans knew me well enough from my previous visits to collect visas for the Beatles to trust me. It's unheard of for them to open up Grosvenor Square on a Sunday, but I wasn't going to complain!

All was well; Robert Stigwood said he'd send round Cream's passports to me and I could relax and go shopping with Lesley. We spent an enjoyable Saturday afternoon in town and came back to the flat at about five o'clock. There was a telegram in a little yellow envelope on the doormat. It read, "Under no circumstances will you leave for America. Brian Epstein."

I was absolutely furious. The tone of the telegram suggested that I was trying to work a free holiday in the States. Since when had Brian needed to add his surname to his communication to me?

I picked up my phone and just kept ringing his number, while Lesley unpacked my clothes, muttering about ungrateful employers. Eventually, at about seven o'clock, Brian answered.

"What did you mean sending me a telegram like that, Brian? I didn't ask to go. I'm just trying to help."

"I'm sorry, Alistair. I was trying to be brief to save money."

"Then why put "Epstein" after your name? Did you think I wouldn't know who it was from?"

"Oh, I am sorry, honestly, but I need you in London. I can't possibly let you go. You've done a great job — Robert's told me all about how you arranged the visas — but it's his problem from now on. I cannot have you out of the country at the moment."

"Fine," I replied. "Brian, that's all I want to know. Now, if you tell Robert I can't go, it'll be final. This is why we've been chasing you for the last two days."

"Please forgive me, Alistair."

"Of course, Brian. Let's drop it."

About half-past two in the morning I was woken by the bedside telephone. When I picked it up, I could hear music and laughter in the background.

"Alistair, it's Brian. Wouldn't you just love a week in San Francisco?"

"Brian ..." I began.

"I knew you would! Have a wonderful time! Call me when you get there. Byebye!"

"Who's that?" groaned Lesley. "Was it Brian?"

"Yes, you know it was Brian," I snapped. "I'm going to San Francisco later on today, love." I'll not write down what she said.

I just managed to arrive at the American Embassy in Grosvenor Square by half-past ten. On guard at the door was a huge marine, looking like something out of Popeye, actually holding a rifle! He marched me down an empty echoing corridor while I looked at the back of his shaven neck. Stamp, stamp, stamp, stop at a big door. Knock. Enter. Massive stamping salute. Sir! I meekly took the visas and was marched out again into the Sunday morning calm, feeling sorry for Ho Chi Minh if this character got his hands on him.

It was about quarter-past eleven when I arrived at Heathrow. Cream weren't expected until twelve, since one of the privileges of being a star is not having to arrive at the airport an hour before you need to. I decided to spend the time with David Blott of Pan-Am, who'd been booking and re-booking my flight, in the Clipper Club, where we were joined by one of the other Pan-Am guys.

"Hello, Alistair, how are you? I've just seen your boss downstairs."

"Brian's downstairs? You must be joking. You must have seen his double. Here at eleven o'clock on a Sunday morning after the night I know he had?"

"I'm sure it was him. Oh, well, I could have been mistaken, I suppose."

About five minutes went by and another guy came in.

"Hello, Alistair. I've just seen your boss downstairs."

"This is suspicious. Hang on, David. I'm going to take a look on the concourse."

Out I went and looked down from the balcony on to the crowded concourse. Yes, there was Brian, looking utterly immaculate as usual. I went down to greet him, wondering why he was there. Could there be a hitch even at this late stage?

"Hello, Alistair. I just thought I'd come and see you off. How are you? Sorry about all that nonsense. I do apologize."

"Brian, you never come to see anybody off. You're either with them or you leave it to me. Come on upstairs to the Clipper Club."

"No, no. I just wanted to see you. I didn't realize you were in the Clipper Club. I wasn't sure you were even here yet. Have a wonderful trip. Ring me when you get there. Say hello to the boys from me."

Off he went to his chauffeur-driven car and away. In all the dozens of trips which we've made through Heathrow, I've never known Brian to come to the airport to see anyone off. He sometimes goes with the Beatles or with Cilla, but he never comes to the airport just to be sociable — and especially not when it isn't even one of his groups who are flying out. Still, he seemed entirely natural and full of beans, which is a delight to see after some of the downs he's had in the last few months.

We're coming in over London, so I shan't record the whole story of that amazing tour just yet. I survived sharing a hotel bedroom with Ginger Baker, had my mind blown by the light show at the Fillmore and got on famously with Bill Graham, the guy who runs the Fillmore concerts.

I was going to fly back yesterday, but then I bought a San Francisco newspaper to bring back as a souvenir for Lesley. It was the size of about fifty of ours! I was just idly flipping through the entertainments page when I saw an advertisement for a Four Tops concert at the Coconut Grove in Los Angeles. NEMS brought the Four Tops over for their first tour of England and I went with them to help them along. Here they were now, appearing just up the road (more or less!). They're a marvellous bunch of guys and we had a great time on the tour. Brian threw parties for them and we went out on the town. What a groove to go and meet them again! Wouldn't they be surprised!

I happened to have a call booked to London, so when it came through I told Brian, "You'll never guess who's playing the Coconut Grove! The Four Tops!"

Brian was delighted, in absolutely terrific spirits. "You are kidding! You've got to stop off in Los Angeles. Never mind coming back here; you're not going to do any work over the weekend, anyway. Stop off and see them and come back here on Sunday. Give them my love and ask them when they're going to come back and do another tour for us. Tell them I want them back in England."

"Right, Brian," I agreed, really happy to hear him sounding so well.

It was a real pleasure to book into the Ambassadors Hotel in Los Angeles and spring a surprise on the Four Tops at the Coconut Grove. We had a terrific reunion and they're going to do another tour with us.

So this is the overnight flight from Los Angeles and I feel like a bit of old shoe leather with all the travelling!

London

Brian is dead.

It's in a hundred newspapers and and a dozen film bulletins. I was there when he was found and I stayed there until his body was taken away. Perhaps it will do me good to record what happened on that day, Sunday 27 August 1967.

Brian had been in the best of spirits when he'd seen me off and when I'd talked to him on the phone from America. There was no reason to be concerned about him at all. I was sitting talking to Lesley early on the Sunday morning, just after I got back from the airport, telling her about the trip to California. I'd just come in and I was looking forward to taking off the denim shirt and jeans that I'd travelled in and having a soak in the bath. We were interrupted by a phone call from Joanne Newfield, Brian's secretary. She said that Antonio and Maria, the couple who acted as Brian's butler and housekeeper at Chapel Street, couldn't get Brian to respond to knocks on his bedroom door. They were sure Brian was in there because the door seemed to be locked. They'd phoned Joanne because they didn't know what to do. She was about to go over to Chapel Street to see whether there was anything wrong.

"I don't really fancy going. I'm sure he's all right. They swear he's there in the bedroom, though. Will you join me at Chapel Street, please, Alistair? I know you've just come in from the States, but I'm a bit worried."

"Yeah, of course," I sighed. "I'll have to take a cab, but I'll be there as soon as I can."

Lesley was doing her nut over this. I'd been away a week and as soon as I got back I had to go running over Brian, without even a chance to collect myself.

I tried to be reasonable. "It'll be one of two things. Either Brian will have already gone out without them noticing or he'll be sitting up in bed asking what all the fuss is about. I'll either be a long time or I'll be back for lunch."

Lesley thought Brian was playing games again. A couple of times in the past Brian had phoned me and made me think he was going to commit suicide. I'd charged round there at high speed only to find him perfectly all right and wondering why I was bothering him. I imagine he'd decided he would do it, then by the time I was on my way he'd decided he wouldn't even bother trying. Still, I had to treat the call as if it might be serious.

Cabs in Clapham South on a Sunday morning aren't exactly thick on the ground, but at last I arrived at Brian's house. Joanne opened the door, looking terrible, with the word, "Upstairs'.

I went up the stairs two at a time and as I was halfway up I heard the sound of splintering wood. Joanne had phoned the doctor because she hadn't been able to get a reply when she knocked at Brian's door. The doctor had put his shoulder to the door and forced it. As I went into the room, he'd just reached Brian's side and was leaning over him.

Brian's bed consists of two single beds pushed together to make an enormous one. He was lying on his side on the bed, seemingly asleep but very white. I knew instantly that he was dead. The doctor finished his brief examination and said, "Yes, I'm afraid he's dead."

I looked around the bedroom. On the bedside table were about five different bottles of pills, all bearing chemists" labels. In the later days, Brian lived on pills to wake him up, pills to put him to sleep, pills to keep him lively, pills to quieten him down, pills to cure his indigestion. All the bottles had their caps properly in place and all of them were still quite full of pills. There was no empty bottle that I could see. By the side of the bed was a pile of correspondence which he'd obviously been going through. There was a plate with about three chocolate digestive biscuits on it and down by the side of the bed there was a glass and a half-full bottle of bitter lemon. There was no sign of a note or a message, no blood, no disturbance in the bed. He just appeared to be asleep with the bedclothes over him.

The doctor and I searched the room for any evidence of what might have happened to Brian, but there was nothing to find. We went downstairs and the doctor called the coroner's office while I told Joanne.

"Oh, my God," she said. "We've got to get hold of Clive."

This is a double blow for the Epsteins. Harry, Brian's father , died about six weeks ago. He and Brian were always very close and Brian and Clive had been heartbroken. Even then the thought was going through my mind that Brian couldn't have committed suicide. He could never have done that to Queenie, his mother, so soon after his father's death. He thought far too much of her to bring her more grief. She'd actually been staying with Brian until a few days before he died.

I poured myself a stiff brandy and thought it through. We had to contact Clive so that he could break the news to his mother before she heard it on a news bulletin or some pushy reporter called her. There was no reply from anyone. Clive was out. I rang Brian's house at Kingsley Hill, hoping to catch Peter Brown or Geoffrey Ellis, two of the top figures in NEMS Enterprises, but they were out too. Time seemed to be standing still, in a horrible limbo.

The doorbell rang. I opened the door and there was a reporter.

"Hello," I said quite calmly. My brain seemed to be working quite normally, but I didn't know when the shock of it would catch up with me.

"I hear Brian's ill," the reporter began.

"No, not at all," I answered, trying to sound confident.

"What are you doing here on a Sunday morning, then?"

"Oh, he called me over to go through some papers with me, but he's gone out for a drive." I prayed that the doors of the garage weren't open and that no one would check whether Brian's Bentley was still there.

"All right," the reporter said, with a look of disbelief, and off he walked, doubtless to check my flimsy story.

The next step was to phone Lesley. She was absolutely wonderful. When she heard the news she just broke down; she was very fond of Brian for all her anger at the way he'd been behaving in the last few days.

"I'm going to be a long time, love," I told her.

About half an hour later there was another ring at the doorbell. There was a messenger with a parcel containing my dark suit, white shirt and tie and a pair of black shoes and socks. Lesley had realized that I was still wearing the denims and sandals that I'd flown back from Los Angeles in. Bless her for the thought.

At this stage the only people who knew that Brian was dead were myself, Joanne, the doctor, the police and the people at the coroner's office. Joanne had spirited Antonio and Maria away to a safe place out of the storm of publicity which was about to break. I don't know how the reporters found out that there was something wrong at Chapel Street, but find out they did. All of them were told the same story, which sounded more and more lame as the day wore on. Even worse, the jungle drums had been spreading the news to the public and a little knot of people began to gather outside in the street. There was a woman with a child in a pram, just standing there looking across the road at the house.

My big worry was that if the press found out the truth, Queenie might find out from the radio. I just kept on ringing Clive every few minutes, desperate to make contact. At last he picked up the phone.

"Hello, Clive. It's Alistair ..."

"Alistair! How was San Francisco? Did you have a wonderful time? Have you seen the Four Tops?"

I cut in as quickly as I could. "Clive, there's been an accident."

"Oh, what? Not Brian?"

"Yes, it's Brian."

"Is he all right?"

"Clive, he's dead." What more could I say?

Clive let out a long terrible scream and dropped the phone. Barbara, Clive's wife picked up the phone.

"Alistair, what on earth's wrong?"

I told her and asked her to try to contact Queenie.

"Don't you worry about us," she said, and put the phone down.

By the afternoon the news broke and the press were about out ears, clamoring for the story. There was nothing I could say that seemed right. A hideous moment came when the hearse arrived with a black coffin to take Brian away to the mortuary. The coffin seemed so functional and impersonal, lined with black baize, a mere vessel for the transport of the dead. I had to supervise Brian's last journey from Chapel Street.

I went round the corner to meet some of the press men, but I couldn't tell them anything. There was one reporter, Mike Housego, who stayed on to sit with me in a little pub round the corner in the mews. Suddenly it hit me and I cracked. I poured out the whole story, all my feelings about Brian. He listened to my revelations like a true mate and acted as a buffer to absorb my reaction — and he never printed a word of it. I saw him a day or two later and thanked him for not taking advantage of me.

"Forget it, mate," he said grimly. "You needed to talk. That wasn't an interview. Let's leave it at that."

At last I handed over to the press office people and went home to Lesley. We spent the evening talking about all the good times we'd had with Brian over the years.

"The thing I'll miss about Brian is his parties," Lesley said. "Everything was just right, always."

On the next day, Monday, I went down to Chapel Street and there were rows of flowers which people had left. I gathered some of them to take them inside. On the top step somebody had left five red carnations beautifully placed in a row, with a piece of paper torn out of a notebook saying, "We loved you too." That finished me. I took them indoors, dashed into the bathroom and cried like a child. After a few minutes I felt better, so I put the flowers in water and placed them on a table with the note beside them.

So there it is. My friend is dead and no one can replace him, either as a friend or as the manager of the Beatles. What a lot we've been to each other over the years since I first went for that interview in Brian's office at Whitechapel. The ambitions, the fears, the high spots, the depressions, the parties, the rows; they all come back to me now.

There's already been a lot written about Brian and there's going to be even more written now that he's dead. Sure he preferred the company of men, but never in all the years that I worked with him did I ever think that he had any homosexual interest in me. It simply wasn't an issue. Why should it be? If he'd been with me in California, he'd have seen the way things are running. In a few years time, nobody would have given a damn who he went out with. Poor Brian, dead before his time.

I'll let the pop journalists celebrate Brian's abilities in management. He took four talented lads from Liverpool and made them into the best-known faces in the world. That is all that needs to be said about his ability to spot talent and develop it.

When he stopped amusing himself by merely spotting which records would be hits and started to remold the hit parade himself, he changed the world, in a way. No one in the entertainment business will ever be so successful as the Beatles, I'm sure, and their success is due so very largely to Brian. But it's more that entertainment; the Beatles represent something else, something to which young people respond in a way they've never done before. I'm just proud to have played a very small part in Brian's magic.

I think back to Brian's treats, like the time he sent me to Sweden to check that Billy J. Kramer's tour was running well. When I came back and said that it had been fine and why had I had to go since there was nothing to do, Brian just said that I'd looked as if I needed a holiday. Another time, he came into the office with tickets for us to go to see Manitas de Plata at the Albert Hall. Afterwards we all went to eat at the Hungry Horse in Chelsea, with Brian picking up all the bills. True, such outings were always only for the men, but to make up for taking me away, he's always sent Lesley a huge bouquet of flowers or a bottle of fine champagne. And all he wanted in return was our loyalty — he had that, and more, from me.

I can never believe that Brian committed suicide. The inquest brought in a verdict of accidental death and that is what I believe. Despite the false alarms Brian had made us go through, I don't think he ever intended to take an overdose. All the evidence in the bedroom pointed to a horrible accident and so did Brian's excellent spirits the last time we met, when he saw me off from Heathrow, and the last time we talked on the telephone, when he was full of ideas for the next tour of the Four Tops. If I needed any more convincing, I'd tell myself that Brian could never have done such a thing to his mother. It was just not in the man.

11
CHAPTER

London

Everything has been very confused since Brian died. His guiding hand has been sorely missed, even though in his last months he rarely appeared in the offices.

The boardroom infighting has been devastating and all I've been doing is keeping my head down and hearing it all going on above me, like a Kentish farmer watching the vapor trails of the Battle of Britain from his field. Perhaps I should have got out straight after Brian's death, but I feel loyalty towards the boys and, besides, Clive Epstein especially asked me to stay on as General Manager of NEMS. I think he sees me as one of the last of the original people and someone he can trust; a minor character with no axe to grind. So I've been passing these unhappy months just dealing with the day-to-day administration.

A change has come, though. NEMS Enterprises has been decisively upstaged by the Beatles" new company, Apple. Apparently, the government takes a kindly view of new businesses being set up and there are generous financial concessions. An operation like this was planned well before Brian died, but Brian wasn't interested in the workings of it all, although he approved of the idea in principle. Since he's died, as you'll have read, Apple has become the special project of the Beatles.

We set up an "Executive Board" of Apple before Brian died, including Brian, the accountant, the solicitor, Neil Aspinall, myself, and then sat down to work out ways of spending the money. One big idea was to set up a chain of shops designed only to sell cards: birthday cards, Christmas cards, anniversary cards. When the boys heard about that they all condemned the scheme as the most boring thing yet. Sure that they could come up with much better brainwaves, they began to get involved themselves. Their idea is that business should be fun. Why should businessmen glare at each other across desks? I quite agree.

After Brian died, Apple started to expand into music publishing, signing new artists, sponsoring inventors and generally putting into practice the principle of making business fun. Business at NEMS Enterprises wasn't fun at all, so a phone call from John a few days ago was very welcome.

"Hello, Alistair. You're looking a bit pissed off at NEMS recently."

"I am, really," I confessed. "All the infighting is getting to me."

"Well, would you like to come and be General Manager of Apple?"

I didn't need a second invitation. I've given my notice in to NEMS and I'll transfer to Apple as soon as I can.

London

So ends another long day in the saga of the Beatles. I don't think some people realize just how much ordinary hard work there is in setting up an office. Apple isn't all sitting around and meditating on the cosmos or digging into great heaps of money. Take the efforts we had to make to find typewriters for the new temporary Apple office in Wigmore Street.

When we moved in, there was absolutely nothing; Neil and I have had to equip the offices from the floor up. When it came to choosing typewriters, we made a list of how many we needed and decided that nothing but the best would do — IBM golfballs. IBM's offices are just across the road, so in an interval between shifting vanloads of furniture into our offices, I wandered over into their showrooms.

I was dressed in a T-shirt and jeans, not exactly the picture of a young business executive, perhaps, but there are plenty of eccentric millionaires who buy Rolls-Royces with cash extracted from dirty old shopping bags. I suppose the snooty young salesman didn't see me as one of that type. He stayed well away from me, but kept a close eye on what I was doing (shoplifting a typewriter?).

When I'd decided what I wanted I called him over. "Excuse me."

"Yes ... sir?"

"This one."

"Sir?"

"I want five of them."

"I beg your pardon?"

"We're Apple. I'm the General Manager. Here's my business card."

Word has got round the business community that Apple is being formed and it didn't take this young sprig more than half a second to change his tone towards me. "I'm terribly sorry, sir. There is a considerable waiting list for these golfball typewriters. I could let you have one on loan."

"I don't want to know about waiting lists. I don't want to know about loans. Can you come up with five of these in the next three days and bring them fifty yards across the road to our new offices?"

There was a lot of fiddling about while the salesman went to ring around, so I went back to our offices. I knew what the reply would be and when he called to say it was impossible I wasn't in the least surprised.

Time for Mr Fixit to put on his thinking cap! This time I came up with the name of Kev Cunningham, who used to play with the Silkie, one of NEMS" lesser-known groups, but is now an IBM salesman in Liverpool. He's managed to find three for me and I've unbent a bit and accepted two on loan, so the problem is partly solved.

Meanwhile, Neil and I are still looking for permanent offices. We've looked at a big place in Hanover Street and another in Regent Street. Now we've heard that there's a place going in Savile Row. Could be interesting!

London

One thing I can't complain about is that life is boring since I became General Manager of Apple! You can't imagine what it's like to see business being done without a thought for expense or profit. Let me show you what I mean.

One Sunday the boys and some of the rest of us were having a meeting at Hille House, just talking generally. Someone came up with an idea: "I tell you who we've got to have. Derek Taylor!"

Derek, the boys" former press officer, was living in Los Angeles, managing the Byrds and the Beach Boys.

"Hey, Alistair, you must have Derek's number!"

"Well, no," I mumbled. "Do you think that this is the right ...."

"Never mind. Find his number and we'll give him a call."

When I at last came up with Derek's number and we'd been connected (it must have been the small hours in LA), the boys took it in turns to persuade him to come and join Apple.

"I don't know exactly what you'll be doing, Derek. We'll think of something. Just pack up and come over to join or fabulous new company!"

Derek and his family packed up and came. Who ever could resist an invitation from the Beatles?

Another time, Paul and I went out to Heathrow to have lunch with an American called Ron Kass, who's a leading record company executive. He was passing through on his way to or from Europe and couldn't come into town to see us, so Paul and I had lunch with him in the Verandah Restaurant at Terminal Three.

"Right," said Paul, "you're coming to join us."

And he did, too.

It seems to me that we're trying to leap before we can walk. Neil and I are just trying to keep the lid on, saying, "Sure, we've got lots of exciting ideas, but don't you think we ought to start slowly and build up?" You can guess the answers we receive!

It's not only people that Apple are buying at tremendous expense without much idea of their role in the company. Take the executive jet, for instance. I was told to research the cost of buying a Hawker Siddley HS125 jet, with full interior conversion, livery, service and so on. I brought all the figures into a meeting and suggested that when we weren't using the jet we should lease it to other companies.

"Oh, stuff that. We don't know when we're going to want it."

"Well, you're going to have to exercise a bit of control. We can make sure it's not leased out on a long lease, even limit the time out to twenty-four hours."

"Oh, bollocks. We want it there all the time."

So died that idea, after all my research. A few days later, if I'd mentioned the jet, they'd have forgotten what I was talking about. I have terrible doubts. Perhaps I ought to resign, but they're my friends and the job is still fun most of the time.

London

The *New Musical Express* has a picture of me advertising Apple — in a rather compromising position!

It's all Paul's idea, as usual. The boys want to bring as many songwriters and performers as they can into the Apple Corps, so they decided to place an advert in the *NME* and to make a poster to paste up all over London. Paul wanted a picture of a straight guy dressed in business suit, bowler hat and shiny shoes, and playing a one-man band! Well, there's really only one man at Apple who's famed for his shiny shoes! The only problem was the bowler hat, but I nipped out into Savile Row and bought one especially for the occasion.

The photo-session was hilarious. There I was, strapped into the one-man band kit: great heavy drum on my back, cymbal, guitar, mouth organ, the lot. Around the stool I was precariously perched on was all the clutter which any singing accountant might have lying about his house: euphonium, French horn, trumpet, violin bow, manuscript paper, copies of the *Writers" and Artists" Year Book* and *Stage* and a cheap tape recorder, supposed to be preserving what I was wailing for posterity!

We tried a few poses with me sitting there looking creative and feeling like a prune, but Paul still had a few suggestions left. "It's no good if you aren't really singing. Sing us something — anything you like."

Well, I can't sing at all, except in the bath. It's always the same, isn't it? Whenever you're asked to say something into a tape recorder to test the mike, you can never think of anything to say. Ask me a question at any other time and I'll talk for hours! At last I hit on a song: "When Irish Eyes Are Smiling', of all things! I hollered this into the mike, hoping that some clever character hadn't really switched it on while I wasn't looking. All the time, the photographer was clicking away happily.

At the end of the session, Paul and I were walking down one of the streets in Soho, while I was flexing my shoulders to get rid of the stiffness that the heavy drum had caused. I'd forgotten that I was still wearing the bowler hat, until Paul snatched the hat from my head, threw it into the street and started jumping on it!

"I've always wanted to do that!" he laughed. We both fell about roaring with laughter and leaning against the wall for support.

When we'd stopped giggling, Paul steered me round to Dougie Millings, the guy who makes the Beatles" suits, and told me to choose any cloth I fancied. He then designed a suit for me, told Dougie to take my measurements, finish it as quickly as possible and charge it to his account. Can't be bad, I thought, a top quality suit in exchange for a bowler hat and a few minutes dressed as a one-man band!

When I saw the ad on the back page of the *NME*, I have to say I was a bit taken aback. I never knew I could look like that. By the way, don't believe all you read in newspapers. I never wrote a song in my life and the nearest I've come to owning a Bentley is buying a Dinky Toy for my nephew!

London

Wow, it's hot! In London today the temperature must have broken all records, but I've been lucky enough to spend the afternoon with George at Kinfauns.

I enjoy being with George; it's always peaceful at Kinfauns and there's none of the pressure to do things that I sometimes feel when I'm with John or Paul. Just sitting indoors listening to George learning to play his sitar is very relaxing and the hours seem to fly by without me noticing.

INTERNAL MEMO
To:
From:
Subject:
Date:
SO YOU THINK YOU'VE GOT TALENT?
Whatever it is – songs, singers, ...
Send it to APPLE
Our address is 94 Baker St. W.1
So you think you're TALENTED?
Most people are.
Singers, songwriters, musicians
Send it to Apple 94 Baker St

Today we were outside, sitting on the grass next to George's little pool. This isn't a swimming pool; it's more like a pond, about six feed wide and a couple of feet deep. George and I talked about all manner of things and in an idle moment he looked at the pool.

"You see that water?" he said.

There were all sorts of tiny little creatures wriggling and swimming around in the greenish water.

A few weeks ago, I filled that pool up with water, clear tap water with nothing in it, and now there are living things in it. Where have they come from?"

We were already talking about life and the great mysteries, so we veered off the subject of the pool on to religion and the Indian theology that George is studying. But that's George. With most people, infested tap water would have led to a discussion about water works and their efficiency, or lack of it; with George, everything leads to the cosmic meaning of life.

London

Although I'm known by the grand title of General Manager, my job is really more and more administrative. The boys choose which projects they're going to support and often there are more things running than I know about. Hundreds of tapes and demos arrive in the postbag every week and they're heard and assessed.

But there are many other schemes afoot outside the music business. Take Alexis Mardas, better known as Magic Alex, the architect of the Greek trips. Alex doesn't look like the backroom scientist or the eccentric inventor. He's got long blond hair and a beard, and he always wears an embroidered sheepskin jacket, just like your average hippie. Alex is a project on his own, one of those geniuses who invent ridiculously simple-looking ways of doing complicated things. Give him a couple of safety pins and a bunch of old keys and he'll probably come up with a computer! Some of his gadgets even seem to defy science itself.

Alex's workshop is in a little mews just behind Marylebone Station and he called me there one day. When I arrived, he was sitting at his desk with his telephone in front of him and his arms crossed.

"Hello, Alistair. We call your office now."

Without moving to his telephone he just spoke my number into thin air. I looked at him as if to say, "So?" A noise of ringing came into the room, then a voice I recognized said, "Mr Taylor's secretary."

"OK. It is me, Alex."

"Oh," replied my secretary. "He's just coming over to see you."

"OK. Thank you."

A perfectly ordinary, even boring telephone conversation, you'll think. But Alex rang my office, spoke with my secretary and broke the connection all without moving from his seat or touching his telephone! The machine was sensitive to his voice pattern, so that all he had to do was speak into it the number that he wanted to reach and the phone would automatically make the connection! I even checked with my secretary when I went back to the office. Yes, Mr Mardas had called. Now there is magic, without a doubt. If the business world knew about an invention like that, there would be mobs outside Alex's workshop greater than the hordes who used to besiege concerts!

Another time I came into Alex's workshop to find it full of beautiful music being played on what appeared to be a very high-quality system. The tape deck was playing and the amplifier was on, but I could see no sign of any loudspeakers.

"That's groovy music, Alex, but where are your speakers?"

Alex pointed to a couple of polystyrene ceiling tiles, each about a quarter of an inch thick. "There they are."

On each tile there was a blob of what looked like glue, and a spiral of the some material leading out to the edge. Set into the centre blob was the finest imaginable copper wire. Could this piece of household junk be producing such wonderful music?

"Come on, Alex. You're kidding me. Where have you hidden the real speakers?"

"I am not kidding. You pull out the wire and the sound will stop. It does not matter. I stick it back in."

I gently pulled out the wire from one of the tiles and one channel of the stereo disappeared!

"That's incredible!"

Alex hadn't finished yet. "I have this idea," he went on, "that we sell rolls of wallpaper with these speakers set in it. That way you have speakers all round your room, whatever height you want. Good, no?"

Amazing! To produce sound of the quality I heard from an ordinary speaker would have needed a cabinet the size of a refrigerator!

Such talent shouldn't go to waste, I thought. Why not ask Alex to solve a small domestic problem for Lesley and me? When I was out in our kitchen telling Lesley about Alex's space-age speakers, she was making some sauce.

"This sauce is bringing me down," she said. "I have to keep stirring it all the time. If I want to go across the kitchen to do anything else, I have to wait, because the sauce will go wrong if I don't keep stirring it. Why doesn't Alex made some gadget that will stir a sauce on its own and let me get on with the other jobs? It'd sell a million!"

I think Lesley was just joking, but I decided to put Alex to the test. I put the problem to him and he went very quiet.

"I will think about it."

Three weeks later, Alex phoned me at the office and asked me to come to the workshop. He had a gas ring there with a pan of water simmering on it.

"Now, you look at this."

Alex took a roughly-soldered metal disc about half a inch thick and two or three inches in diameter.

"Now watch."

He popped the disc into the water. There were no wires, no attachments of any kind and nothing inside the disc, but the peculiar object started going round and round and up and down in just the way needed to stir the water!

"There is your electric spoon."

I wanted to take it away and show it to Lesley, but he wouldn't let me have it. Too roughly made, he said. I should wait until it was properly finished.

The man's mind spins out ideas like a Catherine Wheel spins out sparks. George wants him to install a voice-sensitive lock on his door so that his friends" voices can be programmed into it and they can just walk up to the front door and say, "Hello, it's me," and the door will open for them. Anyone else would have to knock! Alex has designed a tiny throwaway radio supposed to sell for a few pence and made out of a few pieces of plastic. I heard a prototype that would fit in your pocket and looked as if it were made out of the leftovers from a child's construction kit, but it worked just fine. Quite an inventor!

London

Have you ever wondered what you'd spend your money on if you were a millionaire? I can tell you what three very famous millionaires spent some of theirs on a few days ago.

George is a very keen motorist. He even goes down to Brands Hatch and, although Brian would have had a pink fit at the thought of him driving a real race, he's put in a few practice sessions. So he really knows a good car when he drives one. Well, the other day he decided he'd like a new car, a Rolls, naturally.

Off went George to the main Rolls-Royce dealers in London and wandered into the showroom. There in front of him was just the model he wanted, so he reached for his check book and went up to the salesman (does Rolls-Royce really employ anyone so vulgar as a salesman or do the cars just automatically waft themselves to the garages of owners who deserve them?).

"That's a great car. I'll have that."

The salesman took all the details of what George wanted and told him the price. Fine.

There was only one snag.

"There will be a fourteen-month wait for delivery, sir."

"You're kidding!" gasped George. "That one sitting there'll do me fine. Just go and tax it and I'll be in to pick it up in a day or two."

George didn't quite understand the years of tradition behind that salesman's refusal to sell him a Rolls over the counter. Not even for a Beatle will Rolls-Royce make an exception, so George was beginning to feel very irritated. What if the Beatles were to say that there'll be a fourteen-month delivery time on their new single?

Finally, George's chauffeur pulled his sleeve and led him off to a corner. "Let's take a drive and I'll show you a car."

George allowed himself to be driven down the Great West Road towards Heathrow until they arrived at the main import centre for Mercedes. Those guys were definitely not going to let George leave without a new car. They took him up and down rows of gleaming Mercedes, like a general inspecting immaculately turned out troops. At last they arrived at the ultimate — a row of brand new Mercedes 600s. These aren't just cars, they're the future. They stretch from here to next week, you could put a ballroom in the back, everything operates by power — brakes, steering, windows, seats, air-conditioning — and they look like no other limousine on earth. George was in love at once!

No question, George wanted one, in black.

There was one fatal question. Not the price, although it's more expensive than the Rolls, but the delivery delay. The salesman looked at him and said, "Will you be driving it yourself, or will your chauffeur be the main driver?"

"The chauffeur will do most of the driving, but I'll drive myself as much as possible," replied George.

"In that case, Mr Harrison, we'll contour the driving seat to your measurements. We've got to allow five days for that, so we'll deliver it to Esher in six days" time."

Mercedes was as good as its word. Six days later, to the minute, the gigantic black Mercedes 600 turned into the grounds at Kinfauns, contoured seat and all. Perfection. Like anyone with a new car, George wanted to show it off, so he phoned Ringo and said, "Come on over and see what I've just bought."

Ringo jumped into his car, drove over, took one look at the black monster and shouted, "Bloody hell, what a car! I must have one of those." The next morning saw Ringo at Mercedes on the Great West Road ordering a silver Mercedes 600. It was the same story; five days to adjust the contours of the seat and on the sixth day a brand new silver monster was on Ringo's driveway.

The next one on the scene was John. When he saw the two cars parked together, he let out, "Hell, you never told me you'd ordered these! Where did you get them from?"

"We didn't have to order them. It's five days" delivery, John."

Off down the Great West Road went John —and he's got one too! Within a fortnight they sold three of their absolute top model, without any effort. I'm glad I can't afford shares in Rolls-Royce!

Paul has stuck out against the fashion, so far. He's quite content with his Aston Martin DB6 (so would I be!) and his custom-built Mini. That Mini's a fabulous car; it's got everything you could imagine, including a record player! That doesn't work very well when the road's bumpy, as you can imagine. Every so often, Paul and I go cruising down the King's Road with the roof open and the record player going. The only problem is we can't afford to stop in a traffic jam. If we did, the fans would overwhelm us, so we keep scooting from lane to lane, leaving crowds of people saying to each other, "That's McCartney!"

The Beatles still have a Rolls or two. There's George's maroon and black vintage model with his initials on the number plate and Paul has an incredible upright old model painted in blue stripes that he's always saying he's going to take needy children for rides in. Rolls-Royce would go mad if they saw it; at first they discouraged John from ordering black leather upholstery for his new white Phantom. It was considered too common!

As for me, I might be able to manage a two-year-old Mini, if I ever bothered to learn to drive. As it is, there's always a chauffeur-driven limousine at my disposal, so I don't think there's any need for me to drive. Every time I pass a tube station I realize that being an attendant of the rich certainly has its attractions!

London

Paul's just written a song about Martha, his dear Old English Sheepdog. We've had some good times with Martha at High Park, when she set off after Ian's sheep as if she were going to take them to market! A really lovely dog.

Martha has a great friend, Albert, Paul's Yorkshire Terrier. Now, you couldn't find two dogs more different in size than huge Martha and tiny Albert, but they love each other very much and there's one special game that they play.

In front of Paul's house at Cavendish Avenue, there's a paved forecourt which leads to the gates (always locked, of course). Paul sometimes lets Martha and Albert on to his forecourt to play. Martha chases Albert around, then Albert comes snapping at Martha's heels. Without warning Martha suddenly lets fly with one of her great paws and sends Arthur rolling all the way to the front gates, like a tennis ball. Albert is never hurt; instead, he picks himself up and charges back. Biff! It all happens again, but Albert comes back for more!

After about half a dozen thumps Albert usually gets a bit fed up and wanders off round to the back of the house, leaving Martha in possession of the forecourt. Many's the time Paul and I have loved to watch Martha and Albert playing like this, one the boxer and the other the punchingbag!

London

There's no doubt that George and Paul are addicts — of house-hunting. One or other of them is always asking me to look over properties for them. They rarely come near to buying the houses; being in a position to afford them is the main thing, I think.

There's only one snag: if any of the greedy owners were to see so much as a hair of a Beatle's haircut over their topiary, the price would double. So Mr Fixit usually goes down in his role of successful London "entrepreneur" or "import-export businessman', chats to the residents and brings back a report, which is usually filed in the wastepaper basket.

Last week, a gorgeous country house came on the market and George fell in love with the place from the publicity material alone. "This time," he said on the phone, "Patti and I are going to look round in person."

"You can't do that," I argued. "The locals will either force up the price or get up a petition to keep you out."

"Oh, we won't be recognized. Pick you up at ten tomorrow. Just organize the appointment, please, Alistair." And the phone went dead.

I couldn't see how this was going to be done. The boys" faces are on the front pages of the newspapers every week; there isn't a village that hasn't heard of the Beatles. Well, I thought, I can always head them off if it looks impossible.

Promptly at ten the next morning the buzzer in my office went. "Mr Taylor, there is a visitor in the entrance lobby for you."

Damn, I thought. Why does someone have to turn up just when I was due to go out? Irritated, I went downstairs to meet the visitor, who must be guided out of the place as quickly as possible.

Standing in the lobby with her back to me was a young woman in a very expensive but modest costume and a pill-box hat. The very picture of respectability and squareness, I thought. Then she turned round and I positively gasped. It was Patti Harrison —but nothing like the Patti I know so well. "Meet your new wife for today, Alistair," she twinkled. "Now come and meet James, the chauffeur."

Outside the front door, resplendently conspicuous on the double yellow lines was the Mercedes 600 limousine which George recently bought. At the wheel staring dutifully straight ahead was a liveried chauffeur wearing a peaked cap. Patti opened the door and I held it while she climbed in. This isn't much of a chauffeur, I thought. Aren't they supposed to hold the doors open for us?

Then the chauffeur turned round and I was confronted by George's grinning face. "Where to, whack?" Not a trace of Beatles hair was to be seen. It must have taken hours to pin it under his cap.

The house itself is a magnificent pile, owned by a stockbroker whose very county wife showed us round. Patti and I thought we were doing very well as (very) newly-weds, Mr and Mrs J. A. Taylor.

A pity that our chauffeur still had not remembered to open the doors for us when we arrived, but servants are so difficult to find these days, are they not? We looked suitably impressed and talked about all we could do with the house, while the lady looked on us as many ladies in late middle-age do look on young couples. She did a good job of selling the place: "Do you play tennis?" (This as we approached the tennis-court.)

Patti: "No."

Alistair: "Yes."

We tried to give the impression we'd just eloped on the spur of the moment, but as these blunders piled up we began to feel the giggle pressure building inside us!

Eventually we'd seen the whole house, asked all our questions and done very well, I thought. As the lady opened the front door to let us out, there was the Mercedes still parked out front, with George in peaked cap, still looking rigidly to the front.

Cracked it, I thought. The perfect disguise! Then the lady turned to us with a deadpan face and asked, "Are you sure Mr Harrison would not like to see the house as well?'

She'd recognized George at once as we arrived. She was such a good actress, I could have given her a job as my assistant straight away! As it was, we all had tea and talked for ages —but we aren't going to buy the house. What? On my salary?

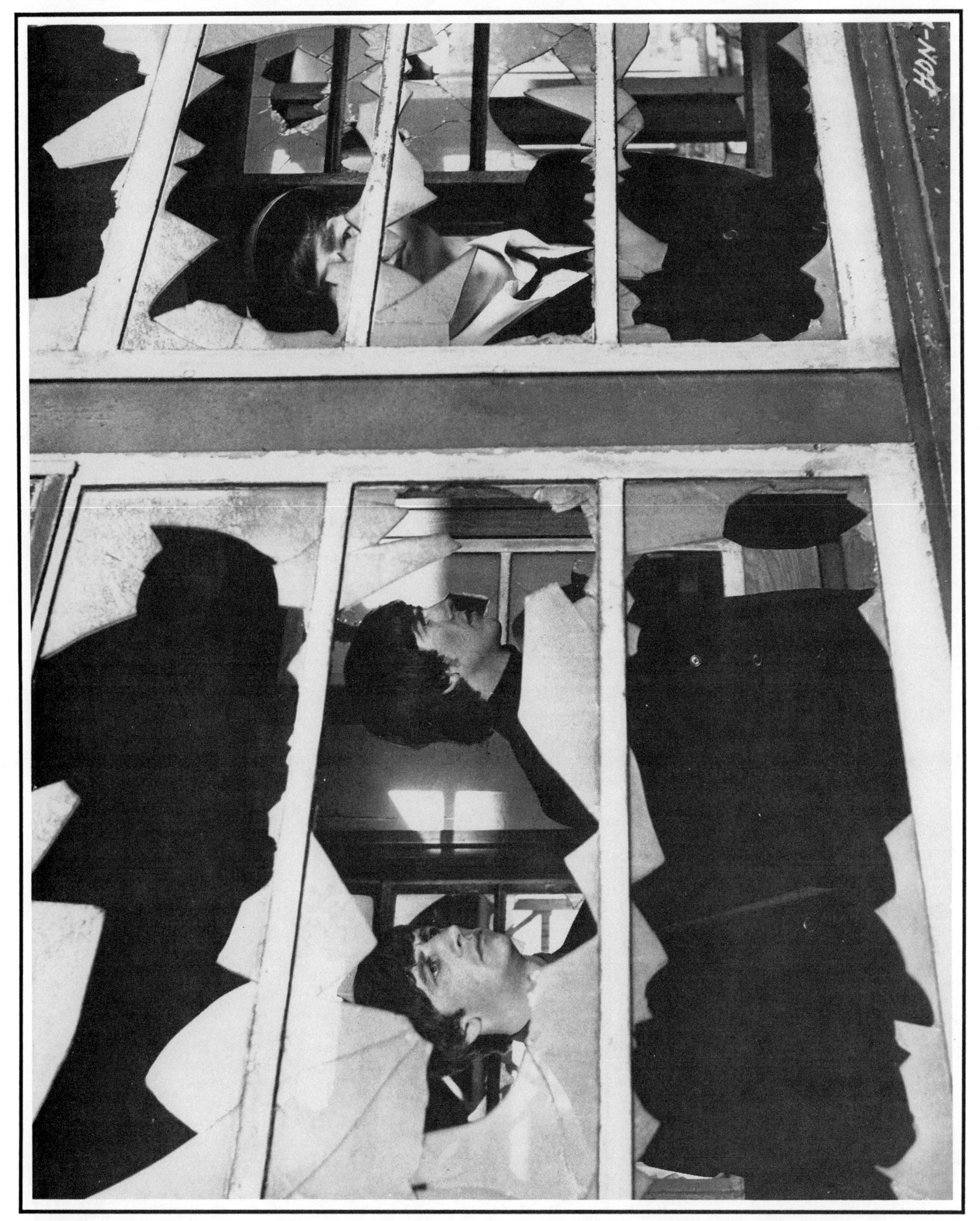

Photos on this and following page from A HARD DAY'S NIGHT (used courtesy Walter Shenson)

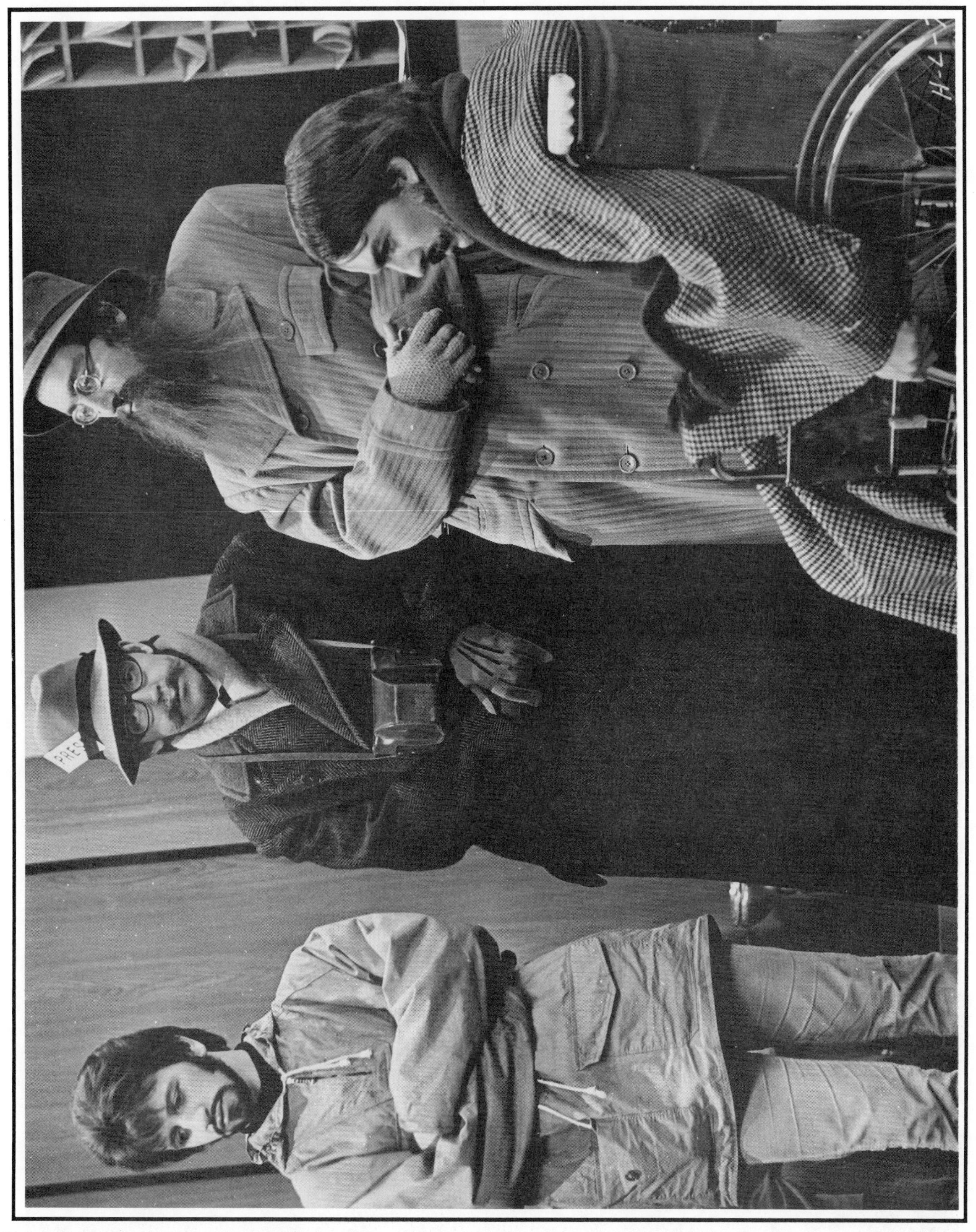

Photos on this and following three pages from HELP!
(used courtesy Walter Shenson)

12
CHAPTER

London

The Beatles are going to make another film!

A couple of weeks ago, Paul rang me up and asked me to come over to Cavendish Avenue straight away; he'd got a great idea. So I charged over at high speed in a taxi, to find Paul sitting on the floor in the big lounge with some large pieces of paper spread out in front of him.

"Hello, Alistair," he said. "Sit down and take a look at these. We're going to make a film! He pushed one of the pieces of paper across to me and I saw that he'd drawn a circle and divided it into slices, like a cake.

"I can see some kind of picture with different episodes in it, like on this drawing. Every slice is a different episode."

We talked it through for a while, as Paul's ideas began to take shape. I'm always amazed by Paul's ability to think of new schemes, which seem obvious when he explains them but are never imagined by anyone else. He aired all sorts of possibilities, until he turned to me and asked, "Do they still do Mystery tours? I can remember, they were always at the seaside, advertised on chalked-up boards. You paid your money and went off in a coach and you didn't know where you were going until you got there."

"I don't know, Paul. I can't remember seeing one for years, but I remember them when we were kids. We used to get on in Blackpool and find ourselves in the Yorkshire Dales for lunch. That sort of thing."

"I'm just thinking," he said, as the inspiration began to flow, "what we can do is have a film about a Mystery Tour, only it'll be a magical one. We can have a courier on the coach to say things like, "Ladies and gentlemen, if you look out of the window, you will see on your left Something Castle." Only, when they look out of the window, they'll see something magical happening which no one expected! It won't bear any relation to what the courier says!"

"Yes, Paul," I said, feeling a bit weak in the face of all this bizarre enthusiasm. "I see."

As he talked, Paul filled each section of his circle with a different idea for a magical happening. I could begin to see what he was driving at.

When the flow of ideas had dwindled a little, Paul put down his pen and asked, "What are you doing at the weekend, Alistair?'

"I've no idea. Nothing special."

"Right. Get down to the seaside with Lesley and just see if you can spot a Mystery Tour. If they still have them, then people will know what we're talking about. Otherwise, we'll have to think of something else."

"Sure, Paul."

Lesley and I sometimes go down to Eastbourne, one of the few retreats we have where we can't be reached by anyone. I didn't mind doing Paul's prospecting there, so we set off for a weekend break. Saturday was a beautiful day, so we took a promenade by the sea, with one eye open for Mystery Tours. Lo and behold, there on the sea front were advertisements for a couple of them. On the Monday I reported the good news to Paul. "Yeah, people will still know what you mean by a Mystery Tour."

Paul was really away by now, the ideas machine in top gear. You'll hardly believe the things he wants to arrange. The idea is that we'll have a travel agency and a whole collection of different characters will come in and book seats on the Mystery Tour. What they don't know is that it's going to be a magical Mystery Tour. We're going to have a fat lady, a dwarf, a posse of vicars and an array of other eccentrics. Pure Beatles!

One thing we need is a brightly colored bus to drive around the country in. It has to be big enough to put all the cast in, together with a very basic film crew who will capture all the action on film as we have our adventures. There's going to be no cheating; we're really going to drive around the country in this bus, with everybody staying in hotels until the location shots are finished.

"Can you get hold of a really bright coach for the film, Alistair?"

This seemed like another good excuse for a weekend in Eastbourne, so off Lesley and I went for another pleasant weekend by the sea. The problem was that the weather gods didn't think the same way and it bucketed with rain the whole time we were there. Ideal bus-hunting weather, I don't think!

There we were having Sunday lunch at the Queen's Hotel, watching the rain pouring down, and I glanced out of the window. I couldn't believe my eyes at what I saw. Pulling in to the car park was an incredibly hideous bright acid yellow and blue coach! I dropped everything and yelled to Lesley, "I've found it!"

I dashed out and buttonholed the driver. I don't think anyone had ever shown such interest in his coach before. We've got to use it!

London

Now that all the other Beatles have put in their ideas, the plans for *The Magical Mystery Tour* have changed about fifty times. John is in a psychedelic phase at the moment and everything's got to be mind-blowing! So the script keeps changing by the day —not that there's really a script, more a set of notes.

What a collection of people we're taking on the Magical Mystery Tour! I've spent hours on the phone to theatrical agencies, booking all sorts of strange acts. On top of the list I mentioned before, there's a group of old age pensioners, some mothers with children, a model, Nat Jackley the comedian, and Ivor Cutler as the courier. You name it and it's there on the bus. Just about the only technical people are a cameraman, a lighting man, a sound man and an electrician —a real skeleton crew. We want everything to be as simple and natural as magic can be! We'll just film things as they happen and see what we come up with.

Since everybody's charging around the country in this horrible bus, somebody's got to work out a schedule of hotels, food stops, even washing facilities. Guess who? At the moment the boys are in Newquay and I've come back to the office to sort out some of our other business. After all, it's not all Magical Mystery Tour; there are other things on the go all the time.

The day before yesterday I was sitting in the office trying to make sense of some of the latest correspondence, when there was a call from the boys. "Alistair, can you get hold of such a thing as a Mae West —one of those big inflatable life-jackets? We've got to have it down in Cornwall by tomorrow morning for this scene we're going to shoot."

I dashed out at once to a shop I know in Albemarle Street (Mr Fixits know where to get anything, even May Wests) and bought one of these bulky objects. The next problem was how to deliver it to the Beatles in Newquay, 250 miles away, by the next morning. There was only one solution; I would have to take the thing down myself. I only hoped the Mae West scene was really vital!

I rang the car company and said, "Pick me up in the morning. We're driving down to Newquay." Of course, that meant I had to get up at about four o'clock, grab a cup of scalding coffee and pile into the car for the five-hour trip. Still, it meant also that I could catch up with a bit of sleep!

When we arrived in Newquay, I found the film set (it isn't difficult to spot the bus!) and went up to the boys. "Hey! look who's arrived! It's Al! How are you doing?'

"Not bad. A bit sleepy. Here's the Mae West, by special delivery."

They looked at the thing in puzzlement for a minute, then one of them said, "Oh, we changed our minds. We don't need it now."

Do they realize that it cost them the price of a chauffeur-driven car all the way from London to Newquay and back to bring that life-jacket, as well as the price of the thing itself? Oh well, that's the boys!

London

Well, the Magical Mystery Tour has rolled its way back to London, so I can take a bit of a break and tell you what has been going on.

We were in Soho this morning at six o'clock sharp with the bus parked across three meter bays; all the people were in Raymond's Revue Bar. Paul Raymond's a good friend of mine and when I told him we needed a stripper for one of the scenes he suggested we use his place.

Have you ever seen a strip club at six o'clock in the morning? Don't answer that. All the glitter which looks appealing at eleven the night before seems tarnished in the cold pre-dawn light. Soho dustbins aren't a pretty sight either.

Anyway, there we were, filming Jan Richmond as she did her strip act to the music of the Bonzo Dog Doo-Dah Band. All the rest of the people, including the boys, were sitting in the audience looking on appreciatively. Suddenly in through the door came two straight-looking guys in snap-brim trilby hats and belted raincoats. Who are these two, I thought. Mafia? KGB? Inland Revenue? They were shown through to where I was sitting drinking coffee, so I greeted them pleasantly enough and waited for them to announce their business.

"Mr Taylor?'

"Yes, " I answered cautiously. Did they want jobs as extras?"

"We are trades union representatives. We have heard about this film That your company is making. We gather it is meant to be a ninety-minute color film."

"Frankly, that's anybody's guess," I answered vaguely. I don't know how long it'll be.

"Is it for television or the cinema?'

"I don't really know yet. At the moment, it's for the sake of doing it. We're trying something new, experimenting and seeing what happens."

"Are you aware of the minimum requirements for personnel connected with the filming of such a venture?" they asked.

I expected that they'd tell me. One did. The other one stuck his hand into the inner pocket of his raincoat and pulled out a typewritten list, just like an official serving a summons. It seems that there's a trades union agreement that says that for any film there must be a minimum number of union people necessary for the making of the film, according to this document. We aren't using more than half a dozen!

"Now, let's have a cup of coffee," I suggested, beginning to understand how captains of industry feel. "Let me explain what we're trying to do here."

They sat down and reluctantly accepted a cup of Paul Raymond's coffee. I opened the bowling by appealing to their professional instincts. "I'm sure you know all about *cinema vèritè* and modern films which try to capture what's going on at any given moment. We're on this coach and we're filming what happens as it happens. Everything that we've done so far has been on location. If we come into the studios, fine, we'll follow your list, but we really don't need anything like the crew you're talking about. They won't fit into the bus!"

"If you carry on as you are doing, Mr. Taylor, we shall black this film and no one will work for you at all. Your whole crew will have to walk out."

"Do you realize you're just killing the whole exercise?" I persisted. "The whole idea is that we're a group of people running round the country in the coach that's parked outside. We only want to film what happens in a very simple way."

All I said made no impression on them at all, but at last one of them said, "You're going to have to pay them, anyway."

"What's that supposed to mean?" I asked.

"Well, as long as you pay all the people on this list, they needn't all necessarily be on the actual set. They've just got to be on the payroll."

I couldn't believe this! Still, it seemed to offer some sort of a way out of the muddle. They obviously needed to justify themselves for saddling us with a bill for the crew that was five times higher than we needed.

"You see, it's designed to prevent films being made on the cheap with skeleton crews. We're only trying to further the interests of our members and to make sure that there's maximum employment."

"Fair enough. I see what you mean. The Beatles are rich, but they aren't stupid with their money. When they see the bill, they'll do their nuts. I shouldn't think they'll bother to make another film. If you'd let us handle it our way, then they'd probably have been making several films a year-and employing your members. We could have come to some agreement, like using a different crew every time. Now this will probably be their last film."

Not even this last argument swayed them. They were as immovable as boulders. At last I admitted defeat.

"All right, then. We'll have to do it your way. But let's understand this from the beginning. If I'm paying for a whole lot of people who I don't need and who aren't going to be on the set, I want to know the telephone numbers of every last one of them. I want them all available all through the working day to suit my convenience and, if I find even one of them not available at any time of the time when I want them, all hell will break out!"

So there we left it. I am to receive a list of personnel and telephone numbers and I will be checking some of these characters to make sure they are available. What a way to do business, though! It's not as if we want to do anything on the cheap; we just want to do it in the way we planned. I'm glad I'm not a Mr Fixit in the film business.

London

Well, *The Magical Mystery Tour* is in the can, as the film people say. We spent this weekend doing the last takes and what a weekend it turned out to be!

I don't think anybody ever really thought through the whole idea of the film. Oh yes, we knew more or less where we wanted to film, but that was just about it. Everybody just piled into the bus and when we arrived we just let things happen. Sometimes it was good and other times it was awful, but we just carried on filming.

The whole project was careening on between genius and absurdity when the BBC began to take an interest in the film. Now that they're starting color transmissions, they want a few really exciting films made with all the effects that will turn an audience on in their sitting rooms. What better than the Beatles" new extravaganza? This means that suddenly we've had to become a lot more organized in every department. The boys have had to work out how long it's meant to be, which scenes must be cut and which added to make any sense even of psychedelic fantasy. And that's where our problems began!

Most of the outdoor and location shots had been filmed by the time anybody came to think about the stack of studio scenes that we needed. Now it's all right hanging loose when you're charging around the countryside with a load of extras who are happy to be paid by the day until you decide you don't want them. Booking studio time's another thing entirely. It turned out that all the usual film studios are booked months, even years, in advance, and not even for the Beatles can an exception be made. Yet here was the BBC breathing down our necks, demanding the film as soon as possible. Yet another call for Mr Fixit, I hear you say.

When one Fixit is in trouble, he turns to another Fixit and this time our saviour was Dennis O'Dell. He's worked on some of the James Bond films and he's built up quite a reputation for making things happen in the film industry, so I contacted him and asked whether there was any way he knew for us to find a studio in double quick time. Of course there is, he said. Now there's a man after my own heart!

Think of the outside of a film studio; what does it remind you of? Yes, that's right —an aircraft hangar! We ended up booking West Malling airfield in Kent. It's an old wartime airfield which hardly anyone flies from these days and it has some very useful big hangars. I think Dennis knew it from other films that have been made there. Anyway, it was the saving of Magical Mystery Tour.

The organization involved in setting up a film studio in an old hangar in the middle of Kent was enormous. There was no mains supply which could handle the massive electrical loads of the lights, so there had to be a huge generator as well as the sound equipment, scaffolding for the scenery, curtains and the thousand and one props needed for the really complex studio shots. Getting an army on the move would have been a simpler job; in fact, I think we were the most exciting thing that's happened in West Malling since the run-up to D-Day!

Our deadline was last night, so there was no time to lose. We simply couldn't afford much in the way of rehearsals; instead we just filmed and hoped. I'm amazed that it's all worked out as well as it's seemed to, considering the number of people involved. You wait until you see the film and you'll know what I'm talking about.

Paul has a passion for Busby Berkeley scenes —the tremendous coordinated dancing that you can see in some of the thirties" films, with hundreds of people dancing in amazing patterns and forming kaleidoscopic pictures on the floor. He insisted that the film should end with a Busby Berkeley type finale. Well, we didn't go quite that far, but we did have the entire Peggy Spencer formation dancing team on the set! The boys, meanwhile, dressed in white tail suits, were to come down a massive staircase (which was built in the hangar in a matter of hours) singing this nostalgic-sounding song called "Your Mother Should Know"! The whole hangar had been dressed to look like a ballroom, with a revolving globe covered in mirrors suspended above the dancers, reflecting light around the walls. You'd never know that the place was more used to engine oil on the floor than Brylcreem!

The very climax of the film was to be when the boys, dressed as magicians, after setting up all these amazing events, lead out a vast crowd of people from the main doors of the hangar. The crowd was to spill out into the blinding sunlight, while the magicians jumped into the Magical Mystery Tour coach and disappeared in a flash. The next problem was how to assemble enough people to make an RAF hangar look crowded. We didn't want just a few dozen there, we wanted hundreds of all ages and types, all under the spell of the magicians.

I think it was Paul who came up with the brilliant idea. "Look, I'll tell you what we can do. Let's invite all the people from West Malling village and all around to come and spend the day on the set watching us filming. We'll lay on all the refreshments, so they can bring the children and the babies in prams and pushchairs and grannies and the dogs and the cats! They can watch all the filming, then at four o'clock or so, when we've done everything else, they can be the crowd in the final scene. We can lead out the Peggy Spencer team and they can all follow us from the hangar. They'll love it!"

What a Brilliant idea! The villagers were really chuffed to be invited and there seemed to be half the county watching the filming. "There are the Beatles in the flesh, not ten yards away, and they seem just like ordinary boys," I could see the people saying. If any day's filming was ever relaxed, Sunday's was. Until about ten to four, just as the extras were being asked to take their positions for the crowd scene.

BANG! Every light in the place went out, leaving us blinking in the watery afternoon sun. This couldn't really be happening, not with only a few minutes of filming left! The news was bad —a gasket blown in the main generator and not a spare within reach on a Sunday in Kent. Our heroic electrician went to work to make a new gasket out of wood and after about half an hour he fitted that one. Hooray, the lights came on!

"Stand by for action, everyone." BANG! The lights went out again. Wooden gaskets don't work. The set was like an overturned beehive with everyone pitching in with more or less useless ideas., as we waited for the man from the company we'd hired the lights from to turn up. And all the time the clock was moving round on this last day of filming and the early autumn sun was becoming weaker and weaker.

Gradually I noticed something. There weren't as many people as there had been half an hour before. All the villagers with children had had enough of watching nothing happening. They'd had their free day out with the Beatles and new it was time to give the children their tea and put them to bed. There was a steady trickle of departing prams and pushchairs and as the clock moved round to seven and opening time, the other people began to make for their locals. If the generator wasn't fixed soon, we'd be filming a scene with no extras, in the dark!

At last the new gasket arrived, but most of the villagers had long since gone home. So the end of Magical Mystery Tour is not what it was supposed to be. If you look carefully at the final shot when it comes out on television, you'll see me, Cynthia Lennon, little Julian, Big Mal, Neil Aspinall, anybody we could lay our hands on —mechanics, engineers, drivers and tea-ladies. I supposed it was as good a way to end the film as any other, but it might look a rather thin crowd!

Now everything goes into the editing stage and God only knows how it will turn out.

London

Oh dear. Didn't Magical Mystery Tour really get panned by the critics? That must be the first time in the five years since 1962 that the boys have done anything that hasn't been a smash hit and they all feel very disappointed.What really hurts is the way some of the critics have taken the chance to try to haul them off some imaginary pedestal by pulling the film absolutely to pieces. As far as I can see, only one small cinema magazine is very complimentary, calling it ahead of its time. I only wonder if all the critics saw it on color receivers; on a black and white set it doesn't look half as good and that mightn't have been too clever, considering that the vast majority of people in this country only have black and white sets.

Actually, the film didn't come out quite as most people expected. I believe Paul did most of the editing and a lot of scenes ended up on the cutting room floor. Nat Jackley had most of his bit cut, for instance. I guess that sort of thing happens with most films —only a very tiny proportion of the film shot is ever shown on the screen.

Now, I would never pretend that Magical Mystery Tour is great art, but it's not a bad first shot by a group of people who are basically musicians with no formal training as film directors. What I liked was the way the boys wouldn't be fobbed off with excuses about why something was impossible. "Why can't we zoom like that?" they asked, and when they got no good answer they went ahead and tried. Sometimes it worked and sometimes it didn't, but at least they experimented with a few new ideas, just the way they do in the recording studios. Still, it is a very self-indulgent film, full of private jokes that only the inner circle will ever understand. I suppose in years to come somebody will get a degree by writing a learned paper on the symbolism in the film. I'd be glad to read it, but all I could add would be that it was all enormous fun and that it hurt no one —not a bad way to spend their money!

London

Merry Christmas and a Happy New Year for 1968 to Beatle fans everywhere! I've had a very merry time recently, especially at the Beatles" Christmas party. After we'd survived the mad rush to finish filming and the dust had settled, the boys came into my office and said, "Why don't we make the party a Christmas Magical Mystery Tour party?"

"Right."

No sooner had I set that rolling when the next suggestion came. "We've been thinking; let's make it a party for all the people who work at Apple as well as a Christmas Magical Mystery Tour party."

"Right," I sighed, adding a few fresh pages to the folder of names to be invited. More than a couple of people on the list.

The final idea followed in short order. "Why don't we make it a Christmas party for the people at Apple and Magical Mystery Tour, but in fancy dress?'

"Far out. Sure you've finished?" I asked.

At last the party took shape. I was determined to do my utmost to make it the best Beatles party ever, so I booked a huge suite at the Royal Lancaster Hotel in Bayswater and hired a designer to decorate it for us. The next job was to hire some good bands to play all night —after all, the Beatles wanted the night off! Finally, the costumes: a matador outfit for me and a Peruvian goddess for Lesley!

A few weeks before the party, Paul came into the office and asked me, "Did you see that group on television last night?"

"No, Paul, I was out somewhere."

"Oh, you don't know what you missed. There was a phenomenal Irish band on. They were fantastic, too much. There's an old guy and two younger guys and a girl. They play this incredible fairy music on some weird pipes. I've never heard anything like it, real fairy music. It just blew my mind!"

"Sounds groovy, Paul. What are they called?"

"The McPeake Family. I've never heard of them before. I wonder if they've made any records? You must try and find out."

Paul wandered off on some other business, but he'd put a thought into my head. Wouldn't it be a surprise if I could hire the McPeake Family for the Christmas party? I lifted the phone and dialled one of my television contacts. Half an hour later I had all the details I needed. It turns out that the McPeake Family are very well known in the circles of traditional folk music. They've won prizes at eisteddfods and been in festivals all over the world. That surprised me, to realize that the music business is in as many watertight compartments as that. I had been sure I knew most of the famous names in most kinds of music. Ah, well.

At the time of the party they were going to be on their way home to Ireland from a long European tour. It seemed too good a chance to miss. Could they stop over in London for a night to come to the Beatles" party? I put the idea to them, mentioning that it would be for the Beatles. Straight away they agreed and promised not to tell anyone where they were going.

On the night of the party, full of secret glee, I put on my matador suit (very slim!) and escorted my Peruvian goddess into the suite. There was John dressed as a rock and roller, Paul and Jane as costermongers in pearly suits and all the Apple gang, most of them totally unrecognizable! Freddie Lennon, John's father, came. The highlight of his evening was when he forgot he was on the stage and fell flat on his face on to the dance floor. No real damage, though.

It really was one of the best nights I can ever remember in all my time with the Beatles — and there was my special surprise to come!

Halfway through the evening I went up to the microphone and said, "I'd now like to introduce you to some fairy music —the McPeake Family!" They were received wonderfully. They produce absolutely marvellous sounds and are totally different from anything else on offer. They play an Irish instrument called the Uilleann pipes (hope the spelling's right), sometimes holding them up, sometimes resting them on their knees. The things are like bagpipes, only different. It was the strangest music I've ever heard, and that's saying something!

John came up to me when they'd finished their set. "Al, I've got to have a set of those. Can you get hold of some for me?"

"Yeah sure, John," I answered, full of Christmas spirit.

Where do you find a set of Irish bagpipes? Why, in Ireland, of course, so I phoned up Paddy, Lesley's brother-in-law in Ireland, and asked if he could track down a pipe-maker. Secretly I wondered if they weren't really made by teams of leprechauns, the sound was so strange.

A week or so later Paddy phoned me back. "Alistair, I've found a guy who makes Uilleann pipes, but he's got a seven-year waiting list."

That's no good to John. When he wants something he wants it now or else the enthusiasm wears off. I've tracked down my own pipe-maker now and I think he can manage to produce them in a year! Who can tell what will have happened to the Beatles in a year, especially after the year we've just been through? Not many people mentioned Brian at the party, but I think he was in everyone's mind. Where will the boys go without his hand to guide them, without his business caution for them to kick against?

13
CHAPTER

London

I suppose everyone knows that Paul and Jane have split up, especially since the press have plastered it all over the front pages. I've heard a thing or two about it all, but I'm not going to spread it all over town, whatever questions I'm asked. I value my friendship with both Paul and Jane too much and I know that neither of them is very happy with the way things are.

This sad business has had one big effect on me. Ever since the split with Jane, Paul's been on his own in Cavendish Avenue and he sometimes can't face going out on the town in the evening. Quite often he rings me up late in the evening and he says something like this: "Al, I'm fed up. Please can you come over and have a few drinks with me." Then I take a cab to Cavendish and Lesley takes an early night.

Sometimes we play records, sometimes we play Paul's instruments and I see him begin to get the idea for a new song. Anything that cheers him up is good news as far as I'm concerned.

The other night I'd gone over to Cavendish and the two of us had a few Scotch and Cokes, not enough to be really tanked up, just pleasantly relaxed. The night had somehow slipped away as we sat around playing records and tinkling away at the piano. Paul suddenly got up and pulled back the curtains. Outside, there was just the first hint of dawn and a sleepless blackbird was tuning up for the dawn chorus.

"Come on, Al," yawned Paul. "I need some fresh air. Let's take Martha for a walk."

"Good idea," I agree, stretching my limbs. Martha sensed what was planned; she unwrapped herself from the rug and her dreams of chasing sheep at High park and started to make for the front door.

We piled into Paul's DB6 and drove the half-mile or so to the foot of Primrose Hill. Leaving the car outside the London Zoo, we went through the fence and started to climb the hill. I remember it was very muddy at the bottom, so much so that Paul turned to me and joked, "So much for the man with the shiny shoes!"

From the bottom, opposite London Zoo and Regent's Park, Primrose Hill looks like a fairly uninteresting mound, criss-crossed by a complex pattern of metalled tracks, none of which seems to lead to the top. There are a few trees about halfway up, but the tip itself is just concrete and grass. Nothing spectacular, until you turn round and look at the view.

From Primrose Hill you can see eastwards and southwards to the far horizon. All London stretches out like a three-dimensional map: St Paul's Westminster Abbey, the giant new Post Office Tower, covered with scaffolding. In the distance, the hills of Surrey and Kent are just visible on a clear day. Focus your eyes nearer and you can see all Regent's Park spread out like a child's toy on the tablecloth, with the Zoo in the foreground.

Paul and I strolled up the tarmac path in the fresh dawn air, while Martha rushed off, chasing imaginary sheep. Apart from the three of us, there was not a soul in sight; we had the hill to ourselves. When we reached the top, the sky was breaking out into a magnificent orange, red and purple dawn. Paul and I sat on the seat, lost in wonder at the sky and listening to the sounds of the zoo waking up below us.

That's an amazing experience in itself. Five o'clock in the morning must be one of the few times of the day when it's possible to hear sounds in London without the background roar of traffic. First of all the birds in the aviaries join in the dawn chorus, adding to the sparrows" and blackbirds" songs like prima donnas guesting at the local operatic society. Then a lion yawns and stretches, roaring for his breakfast, or one of the elephants trumpets in pleasure at the thought of another warm day to remind him of his real home in Africa. There's the whole world in that sound.

It was a bit chilly and there was a fair breeze on the top of the hill, enough to rustle the kites which had been abandoned high up in some of the trees near the gates. Every so often Paul and I would take a stroll round to keep the circulation going.

"Look at that dawn," whispered Paul. "How anybody can say that there's no such thing as God, or some power bigger than us and stand and watch that sky..." We were totally absorbed in the sights and sounds of the universe in front of us as if we were the only men in an abandoned city.

"Got to get back, I suppose," said Paul regretfully, after about half an hour.

"Martha!"

We turned round to go and suddenly there he was standing behind us. He was a middle-aged man, very respectably dressed in a belted raincoat. Nothing in that, you may think, but he'd come up behind us over the bare top of the hill in total silence. Paul and I were sure he hadn't been there only seconds before. Hadn't we been looking for Martha in that very direction?

"Good morning," the stranger said, in an even, pleasant voice.

Paul and I looked at each other and I replied, "Good morning."

"My name's John."

"Mine's Paul. This is Alistair and that's Martha the dog."

"It's lovely to meet you," the stranger continued. "Isn't this wonderful?" And he walked away.

Paul and I looked at each other and I said, "God, that was peculiar." I looked around and there was no sign of the man! He'd just disappeared from the top of the hill as if he'd been carried off into the air! No one could have run to the thin cover of the nearest trees in the time we had turned away from him, and no one could have run over the crest of the hill.

Paul and I both felt the same weird sensation that something special had happened. We sat down rather shakily on the seat and Paul said, "What the hell do you make of that? That's weird. He was here, wasn't he? We did speak to him?"

"Sure. He was here only seconds ago," I said.

"Let's go home," muttered Paul. Suddenly we both felt as though we'd been shouting in church.

Back at Cavendish we spent the rest of the morning talking about what we'd seen and heard and felt. It sounds just like any acid tripper's fantasy to say they had a religious experience on Primrose Hill just before the morning rush hour, but neither of us had taken anything like that. Scotch and Coke was the only thing we'd touched all night. We both felt that we'd been through some mystical religious experience, yet we didn't care to name even to each other what or who we'd seen on that hill top for those few brief seconds.

London

Lesley and I have a charming house guest for a few weeks, a folk singer from Wales who Paul discovered and signed for Apple. Her name's Mary Hopkin and she's going to be a very big name very soon, if I'm any judge. As yet, though, she's very new in town and so we all thought it would be kind if Lesley and I invited her to come and stay with us until she's settled into London life.

She's no trouble at all as a guest. Whenever Lesley asks her what she wants to do she always says, "I don't mind."

The conversations go something like this:

"What would you like for breakfast, Mary?"

"Oh, I don't mind."

"Come on, you're always saying you don't mind. Now what would you really like?'

"I don't mind, really I don't."

"Oh, if you say you don't mind once more, I'll bend the frying pan over your head!"

"But I really don't mind."

Bless her.

Last night we took Mary out on the town. *Yellow Submarine* was having its World Premiere at the Pavilion and we'd arranged a party for afterwards. Rank owns the Royal Lancaster Hotel in Bayswater Road and they've opened a discotheque called "Yellow Submarine"! Where else could we have gone for the party?

Now Lesley and I were going to the premiere and the party and of course we wanted Mary to come as well. The difficulty was finding an escort for her. At this sort of event, reported in all the right papers and magazines (and a few of the wrong ones!), the ladies are supposed to have male escorts. Mary had no escort, as she is so new in town.

This is a simple Fixit, I thought. We have this new American singer called James Taylor, who has just come over to try his luck with Apple. Why not fix Mary up with an escort and a little bit of publicity by suggesting that James and she go to the event together? They're both young Apple rising stars and I thought they'd look well with each other, not in a romantic sense, of course, but just because they're both young and attractive and breaking into the scene at the same time. Fine, everyone said, and I ordered two limousines, one for Lesley and me, the other for Mary and James.

Early yesterday evening, James arrived at the flat while Mary was still preparing herself for the big night out. It was only then that I began to wonder whether I'd made the right decision, because James didn't say more than two words to Mary all the time that we were in the flat. The atmosphere was really awkward but I put it down to shyness and saw them off in their limousine to the Pavilion, still thinking that the evening was going to be a success.

I didn't see either of them to speak to properly until we'd all arrived at the "Yellow Submarine" discotheque. It was a fabulous party, everybody busy enjoying themselves and dancing and generally having a whale of a time —except Mary. Lesley gave me a nudge and nodded towards where Mary was standing all alone. James was nowhere to be seen.

"Where's James, then?" I asked her.

"I don't know. He's gone," she replied, looking slightly lost, but not exactly heart-broken.

I'm never entirely off duty, even at this sort of party, so off I went looking for James. After a few minutes, it was pretty clear that he wasn't indoors, so I cast around outside and found him there. He hadn't any thought for Mary; he was much more interested in what he was smoking!

This was a sudden problem. If you invite publicity, you've got to expect people to be interested and the last thing I wanted was a photographer coming in on this scene. I persuaded James into a taxi and packed him off home to bed, followed by an audible sigh of relief from me. Then I returned to where Lesley and Mary were waiting.

"I don't think James is too interested in staying any longer."

Mary looked relieved not to have to try to be sociable towards someone who'd shown no interest in her at all.

"Well, I'm the winner, aren't I?" I said, turning to both of them. "I came here with one lovely lady and now I've got two to entertain!"

London

George Harrison is a lovely man. I don't often write about him, probably because he doesn't ask me for very much and he doesn't often need rescuing!

We were all up at the studios recording with Mary Hopkin. Of all the people who have come to the Apple label, I like Mary the best. She's got a beautiful voice and a winning presence on stage, but most of all, she's a very graceful and modest person. Anyway, there she was, playing the ordinary acoustic guitar which she always uses, with the rest of us listening to her with pleasure.

While George thought that no one else was looking, he called Mal Evans over and whispered something in his ear. Mal grinned and slipped out of the door. When he came back, a couple of hours later, we were all taking a break and sitting around chatting. Mal was carrying a gleaming guitar case that was obviously brand new. When he went up to George, though, George blushed and looked embarrassed, as if to say, "No, you do it." Mal then walked over with a great beam on his face and presented the case to an astounded Mary.

"George would like you to have this."

When Mary opened the case, lying inside was a beautiful Martinez —the best guitar money can buy, the kind of instrument that top players queue up to put their names down for at about four hundred pounds.

Mary was taken completely by surprise. But George's attitude was typical of him. He liked the music she was playing and thought that she deserved something better to play it on. No fuss, no display of the great man giving the new artist some help, just a quiet presentation by the roadie. George is a lovely man, indeed.

London

Quite often one of the Beatles has an idea and then suddenly a song is being written. I suppose Paul is the one whose skill leaves me with most wonder.

Paul is one of those rare craftsmen who make their skill appear so easy that it seems the most natural thing imaginable. For him, songs hover in the air all around and have merely to be plucked, polished and performed.

Mary Hopkin had just recorded "Those Were The Days" and one evening I found myself in Studio Two at Abbey Road with her and Anne Nightingale. All the boys were there recording, but they'd stopped for a break and Paul had come over to where we were sitting by the piano. He sat down on the piano stool and we all chatted for a few minutes.

The conversation came round to composing and Paul asked Mary, "Do you write songs?"

"Well," replied Mary hesitantly, "the music's all right, but I have trouble with lyrics."

"Oh, but lyrics are dead easy. Lyrics are all around you. Let me show you."

Paul turned round to the piano and lifted the lid, inviting Mary to sit beside him. He played us the first song he'd ever written, which was a three-chord number, then he showed how he's progressed to five chords and beyond that.

"Right," he said. "Let's write a song here and now. Let's think of a story-anything at all.

"Now suppose there's a guy who waits every morning at the bus-stop and there's this gorgeous girl who always stands next to him in the queue. But he's dead shy; he can't bring himself to talk to her, so he feels very frustrated." Paul picked out a tune and started to set the lyrics for this situation to it.

We sat in silence, not wanting to break his spell.

"Now one dark night he goes out to post a letter at the letter-box on the corner. Just as he's putting his hand up to the opening, the girl appears from the other side and does the same thing."

More lyrics, a stronger and more confident tune emerged.

"They both jump back in surprise, but they're both startled into talking to each other, which is a good job, as she's as shy as he is. They fall in love and live happily ever after."

By this time, the song had skeleton and flesh. It was hummable; it worked well.

"You see, that's how to write a song," concluded Paul, and he swung round on the piano stool, quite unaware of how much he had impressed us. It was like one of us saying, "You see, that's how to boil an egg."

Later I asked Anne, "Are you going to write about that in your column?"

With a wry smile she answered, "How could anyone write about what we've just seen?"

Perhaps the song, which never had a title, would have been another Beatles Number One, perhaps not. The awesome thing to me was that Paul could just reach into some space where the rest of us couldn't go and pull out another tune, another set of lyrics —just like that.

Another time, not long after his split from Jane Asher, I was with Paul at his house. We talked about all sorts of things and finally asked, "How do you write songs, Paul? Not many people can do it, but those who can never explain how to those who can't."

"Oh, there's nothing to it. Look, let's write a song together."

"What? You and me? Now?"

"Why not?'

Paul marched me into the dining room, where he had a marvellous old hand-carved harmonium. "Come and sit at the other end of the harmonium. You hit any note you like on the keyboard. Just hit it and I'll do the same. Now whenever I shout out a word, you shout the opposite and I'll make up a tune. You watch, it'll make music."

"Fire away," I said nervously, feeling like someone suddenly asked to be co-pilot of an airliner.

"Black," he started.

"White," I replied.

"Yes."

"No."

"Good."

"Bad."

"Hello."

"Goodbye."

And so it went on until we ran out of pairs of opposites and went to freshen the drinks. I've no memory at all of the tune. You have to remember that melodies are as common around the Beatles as bugs in May. Some grow into bright butterflies and others shrivel and die. I wonder whether Paul really made up that song as he went along or whether it was running in his head already. Shortly afterwards, he arrived at the office with a demo tape of the latest single —'Hello,Goodbye'!

On another occasion, the stars were shining down from a frosty clear sky as Paul and I walked out of Abbey Road studios at 3 a.m. We were tired and looking forward to a Scotch and Coke at Paul's house in Cavendish Avenue. Following us at a respectful distance were two fans; they didn't approach us, being happy just to follow Paul.

High up on a wall at the corner of Cavendish Avenue is an ancient lamp like an old gaslight. Paul stopped, the dim rays of the lamp showing his ankle-length brown tweed coat and his acoustic guitar, which was suspended from his neck by a piece of frayed string.

"I've just written a new song. Would you like to hear it?" he asked.

And he gently took his guitar and standing in the pale cone of light, sang very quietly, a haunting song about a blackbird with a broken wing. Paul's plaintive, boyish voice was the only sound in London, it seemed. Several yards away, the two fans stood, still silent, happy that their long vigil had brought them this reward. Paul sang the song once, beautifully, in that chilly street and then he slung the guitar across his shoulder and casually broke the spell.

Later, Paul played me the demo tape of "Blackbird'. I was terribly disappointed that he had used all sorts of production effects which smothered the delicacy of what I'd been privileged to hear. A second demo even had bird noises added! Paul never could stand leaving a hole in a song unplugged. As it stands today on the White double album, the song has acoustic guitar backing, but with bird noises. How I wish I could recapture the sound of that voice echoing quietly among the curtained suburbs!

London

Paul and I are on the property hunt again, which means that I've been going the rounds of the estate agents. Yesterday I thought that I'd come up with an absolutely idyllic place, out on the border of Surrey and Sussex. Paul and I drove out to have a look at it, picking up the key from the local estate agents, since the house is unoccupied at the moment.

As soon as we arrived, we thought that it was almost perfect. The house had superb views across downland country to rolling hills and the whole setting promised the peace which Paul needs. It stood in an acre or so of garden, with a wooden guest bungalow, a swimming pool and every feature that Paul wanted, but there was one small problem. It stood at the junction of two lanes which ran down on either side of the property. This wasn't too bad from the point of view of security, since a tall thick hedge bordered the whole grounds, and we were sure that we could make the place safe from invasion.

We were discussing the problem of security as we walked back into the house. I could see that Paul was very taken with the place; indeed, he was already working out which rooms would be used for what and which walls could be knocked down to make the rooms bigger. But he was disturbed about the price —it was just too reasonable.

"There's got to be something wrong with it at this price, but I just can't spot it," he agonized.

"I don't see why," I said. "It doesn't smell damp and there are no cracks. Anyway, we can always have it surveyed before you decide."

"Yeah, I love the place. It's great, but something's making me uneasy about it," he insisted.

Down in the kitchen, Paul started to open some of the wall cupboards, heaven knows why, because storage space is usually the last thing he bothers about. Most of the cupboards were empty apart from the lining paper, but as he opened the last one a big rolled up sheet of paper fell out. Out of sheer curiosity we unrolled it and read it. It was a very detailed map of the whole district with the house and the next door bit of open land heavily marked. I noticed some sheets of paper also in the cupboard, so we read these and found out why the house was so cheap.

The local council, according to these papers, had given permission for the patch of land next door to this beautiful house to be developed as a gravel pit! Not only will there be an enormous noise and clouds of dust, but they've also granted leave for the little lane that runs along the side of the house to be the main access, used by dozens of heavy trucks for up to twelve hours every day! We struck the house off our list straight away.

So much for the estate agents! Nobody even mentioned this delightful feature of the desirable residence to us. Even if we'd had it surveyed (which the boys rarely bother to have done) the plans for the next door land wouldn't have emerged. It was just sheer luck that Paul had opened that cupboard and the plans had fallen at his feet. Typical of him!

14
CHAPTER

London

This has been what you might call a travelling weekend. I've been to Sardinia and back — twice! It all started when Paul rang me up from a recording session at Abbey Road in the middle of Friday morning.

"I want to go away to the sun for the weekend with my cousin and his girlfriend. Pick me up in the car from Abbey Road at midnight tonight and run me home first. I don't much care where we go, as long as it's in the sun. Oh, and I want you to find a girl called Maggie McGivern, who's a waitress in that club I went to in Chelsea last week, and ask her along as well. I've lost her address, that's the problem. Anyway, I'll leave it to you where we go; just pick me up at midnight."

There were three little problems landed on my lap in short order: find a warm, sunny spot at twelve hours" notice, organize the transport, and find this girl, whose address Paul didn't even know!

The first two problems were fairly easy. Sardinia seemed to be a good place to go; I don't know why, perhaps because we've never been there before and it's a secluded sunny spot. The only really tricky bit was finding Maggie McGivern and telling her that Paul McCartney thought she was in need of a holiday! Off I shot to Chelsea and arrived at the club, only to find that it was shut! Luckily there was someone who could tell me where this girl lives, so I went around to tell her the good news. She lives in a tall building in Chelsea, and as I rang the doorbell, a window about three storeys up opened and a blonde head appeared.

"Who is it?"

"Are you Maggie McGivern?"

"Yes."

"Can you come down? I don't want to shout in the middle of the road."

When this pretty petite blonde opened the door, I told her who I was and said, "Right, you're off on holiday for the weekend with Paul McCartney!"

"Great! Wow!"

Who'd say no to an offer like that? Of course she agreed and I arranged to pick her up in the car at about eleven o'clock. I shouldn't think she minded missing a couple of nights" waitressing!

I decided I'd go with them to the airport, just in case there were any last-minute hassles. Everything went very smoothly: Maggie was ready at eleven o'clock, Paul was all set to leave Abbey Road at midnight and we all arrived at Luton airport at about one o'clock in the morning. Everybody was on the private jet and I was about to turn round and go back to London, but Paul had other ideas. "Come on, Al. Come with us just for the ride. You can wait while they service the plane in Sardinia and come back with it in the morning. Then you can come back in it and pick us up on Monday. Come on, you know you'll enjoy it."

I didn't think I'd pass up the chance of an hour or two in the sun, so I rang Lesley and told her I was off to Sardinia for a few hours and I'd be back in the morning! Then I took my place and settled down for a superb luxury flight.

A few seconds after the pilot let us know that we were about to touch down, the plane started to bank steeply, until we were going round and round in circles at an incredibly silly angle. When the glasses started to slide off the tables, I decided that I'd better go and talk to the pilot and find out what was going on. That's the advantage of hiring a private jet—you can go and ask the driver what's happening. The disadvantage is that sometimes you'd be better off not knowing!

As the plane started what felt like its fifth complete circuit, I undid my seat belt and staggered down the gangway to the cabin. There I found the co-pilot looking down at the ground through the window beneath him. I tapped him on the shoulder and he removed his head-set and turned to me.

"What's happening?" I asked. "Why are we going around in circles?'

"The bloody Italians have forgotten to put the landing lights on," he snorted. "We can't see the bloody airstrip! You look out the other side and see if you can spot it."

I didn't need asking twice. Swirling about above the mountains of Sardinia at half past three in the morning didn't seem the sort of thing that I wanted to do for very long! At last we spotted the parallel lines of landing lights. Thank God for that! The pilot straightened the plane and set us gently down on the tarmac.

Alghero airport is not exactly Heathrow; in fact, it's more of a military base than a commercial airport and there's only a rough, hangar-like building which serves as reception area, passport control and customs post. At four o'clock in the morning it was a absolutely dead. At last a very sleepy-looking customs officer came stumbling out with a look on his face that showed how much he appreciated being woken up at that time to receive a private jet. He just waved us through and went back to his office.

As we went through the building suddenly all the lights came on and we could see a little bar and a souvenir shop, all within the main building. Another door opened and out walked an immaculately dressed waiter in a crisp white linen jacket and bow tie, looking as if he'd just stepped out of a bandbox! We all stopped dead in our tracks when he announced in a thick Italian accent, "Good morning. You like a drink?"

These licensing laws didn't seem half bad! We all sat around for a while and had a few drinks. Paul started to wander round the souvenir shop and came back with some cork postcards which he'd bought. We all fancied some of these, which are a kind of local craft, so we bought some more packets and spent a few minutes writing postcards to our nearest and dearest and putting them in the local postbox. It didn't seem right for me to bring them back in the jet and post them in Luton!

At last I put Paul and the others in the hire car and off they drove in the early dawn light to their hotel. I wandered back to the jet, to find that there was a hitch with the refuelling. The guys who do the refuelling don't start work until much later, so we had to kick our heels until they came on duty. I was just sitting there in the warmth of the early morning sun, just relaxing and staring into nothing, when the co-pilot came along and tapped me on the shoulder.

"Come on, I'll show you why we didn't want to risk coming in without the landing lights being on."

"What's that?" I asked, rather dozily.

"Just turn round and you'll see."

I did and wished I hadn't. There were two mountains: the plane had flown between them with no more than a few wingspans to spare. I shuddered to think that we might have had to come through that tiny gap without the help of the lights!

London

Paul is a factory for ideas. Just to walk down the street with him is enough to prove that he can see things that the rest of us can't. He and I can stand side by side and he'll see something that never occurred to me. Take the other day, for instance.

Paul and I were walking in the street near the flat in Montagu Place that Apple has bought for my use, idly talking about James Taylor, the new American artist that Peter Asher has signed up for Apple. He's not a bad singer, but the trouble is that no one in this country has heard of him yet. So we were walking, discussing ways of presenting James Taylor to the unsuspecting world.

"Christ! I've got it! shouted Paul, suddenly stopping and staring up at one of the shops we were passing.

"What are you talking about?" I asked.

"Look up there, Alistair."

There above us was a shop sign standing out from the wall: "James Taylor —Orthopaedic Shoes'.

"Good God!" I gasped. "How did you spot that?"

"That's just what we need," Paul carried on, not even listening. "What we'll do is go in and see the guy who owns the shop, pay what he wants, clear out the window display and take a picture of James Taylor standing inside the shop window under the sign. It'll be great publicity!"

It's my job to pick up these ideas that Paul throws out like ash from a volcano and do the fixing that is needed to transform them into reality. Nobody produces ideas quite like Paul, as I keep saying. John sees different things in his own way, but Paul has an eye for what will please an audience. I really must find the time to make the acquaintance of Mr James Taylor, the Orthopaedic Cobbler!

London

I'm so furious I can hardly be polite to anyone, so I've put a Do Not Disturb sign on the door.

You know that today sees the release of the boys" new single "Hey Jude'. We're really excited about this one; it's the sort of record that makes you feel anything's possible. God, how far we've come since the boys were singing "Yeah, Yeah, Yeah" and shaking their heads like feather dusters in a washing machine!

Still, I'm wandering off the point. It's always a good idea, even with a Beatles record guaranteed to sell in millions, to arrange some kind of publicity to make everyone see what's new. We hadn't got around to thinking of anything for "Hey Jude" and the idea of special publicity had somehow slipped away.

Suddenly, yesterday afternoon in rushed Paul, like a little boy who's found that he can slide on ice. "Hey, Al, I've had a great idea. Why don't we use the Apple shop in Baker Street to advertise "Hey Jude"?"

"But it's totally empty. We haven't thought about what to do with it yet," I replied weakly.

"Well, that's it! Don't do anything except paint HEY JUDE in huge white letters on the front window. Everyone knows that it's our shop. Most people look in as they go past to see if we're doing anything. It'll be like a big poster on one of the busiest streets in the West End —and all for nothing! It's dead simple. Any fruit and veg man or butcher could do it in five minutes. You know —"Best Tripe In Today" or "Fresh Pigs" Trotters". Just get some paint or whitewash and a few brushes and send it round there. I'll get Big Mal and a mate or two and do it tonight so that tomorrow's rush hour will stop right in front of it! HEY JUDE — the new Beatles single!"

It seemed simple enough, but then Paul has always had a flair for publicity. I rang around the local stores and had the materials sent round to the Baker Street shop. The only thing that I couldn't get in the West End was whitewash —there isn't much call for it! They had to make do with emulsion paint.

Me, I went home at six o'clock. Not my scene, house-painting. After all, that's how Adolf Hitler started! At about eight o'clock my doorbell rang. There was Paul, a little paint-spattered, but with his infectious grin turned right up full: "Come on, Al. We're having a great time. Come and join us."

Who can resist a real enthusiast? I put on some sloppy clothes and off we went to Baker Street. There were Paul, myself, Big Mal and another guy. This really did seem like five minutes" work, until Paul had another idea. It was too simple just to paint the words on the window. What we were going to do was paint the whole window, then wipe out the title! I never realized how big a shop window could be! My arm was aching after about half an hour, so we all knocked off, had a Scotch and Coke, then went back to it. Paul wanted HEY JUDE on the front window and the title of the flip-side on the side window. Who buys a flip-side, anyway?

Rubbing off the newly-dried emulsion paint was the worst bit, but we finished in the early hours of the morning, all of us tired but happy with the result —and with the Scotch!

Words can't describe how I felt this morning when I dragged myself out of bed and arrived at the office. The police came round to tell us that the front window of the Baker street shop had been smashed during the night. All that effort and some bastard vandal gets his kicks by smashing it. I haven't told Paul yet. He'll be even angrier than me.

There, I don't feel much better, but I've rattled the bars of my cage a bit. Back to work now, starting by looking up glaziers in the telephone directory, I suppose.

The police rang a few minutes ago. It seems that the "vandal" has confessed. He's a middle-aged Jewish gentleman who was driving past the shop just before dawn. He'd had a drink or two, and the sight of those words HEY JUDE had taken him right back to the Thirties in Germany. The Nazis wrote JUDE in great white letters on houses and businesses owned by Jews and it was then an open invitation to the thugs and bullies to come along and smash them up. Just seeing HEY JUDE there on the shop window was enough to trigger the old anger. Before he knew what he was doing, he'd thrown a soda syphon which had been in his car through the shop window. I'm not surprised.

The police asked us if we want to press any charges. No way. I don't know if our apologies will make him feel any better, but I'm going to tell him how sorry we all feel about being so thoughtless —and we'll try to keep this one out of the papers.

London

Yesterday I went to prison for the Beatles! I haven't been arrested yet, but I have been carrying mysterious packages around London like a spy in a film.

Yesterday morning I was just looking out of the window watching the rain streaming down the streets and thinking that I could spend a quiet Saturday morning reading the paper with my feet up. Not so. my little dream was shattered by a phone call from Paul. Could I lay my hands on £1118s in cash at once?

Nobody around here deals in cash. We've got checkbooks, credit arrangements, dozens of accounts, but there are no mountains of used fivers lying around. When I asked what it was for, Paul told me an amazing story.

It turned out that the mate of a guy called Scott had phoned Paul earlier in the morning and asked for a pay-off for Scott, who had been taken to Brixton prison on Friday night after failing to keep up with the maintenance payments to his ex-wife.

The other guy told Paul that Scott ran a little band in London called the Ob-la-di, Ob-la-da Band. So what, you may ask. Well, Scott had hit upon the idea of saying Paul had taken the title to the song "Ob-la-di, Ob-la-da" from the posters advertising the band round south London. Of course, Scott's mate had told Paul that Scott would be happy to drop all claims to the title and not cause any fuss if only Paul would arrange for the £1118s Scott owed to be delivered to Brixton prison at once. Now there's a sophisticated form of begging!

Paul couldn't remember whether he'd ever seen the posters. After all, sometimes an idea comes into his mind and who can say how it arrived there? Anyway, although Paul hadn't deliberately used the words, he felt a bit sorry for Scott. The guy wasn't a murderer or a wife-beater; he was just another musician fallen on hard times. Paul was willing to make a one-off payment of the maintenance money on the understanding that Scott was to sign a receipt and write a statement saying he wouldn't be back for more. I reckon that Paul was more than generous to do that, especially as he can't ever remember even seeing the posters.

My problem was simple. Scott would be up in a special court later on in the morning, but would be taken back to Brixton as soon as that was finished, where he would stay until the money was paid. It had to be cash, and it had to be delivered to the prison. OK, I said, leave it to me. But where the hell was I to find £1118s at ten o'clock on a Saturday morning? Another job for Mr Fixit loomed large.

The only guy I could think of was an old friend in the film business, a bit of a fixer, like myself. He's a racing man and there was a chance that he might be able to lay his hands on large amounts of cash at inconvenient times. Perhaps I'd better not mention his name, as I wouldn't like to think where the money originally came from!

Luckily, he was in when I phoned him. I explained the problem and pleaded for help.

"You've got to be joking," he laughed. "It's Saturday morning!"

"I know that, but I've just got to have that money. Paul didn't say so, but I pick up the idea that Scott might start accusing Paul in public of using his title if he isn't out of Brixton by the end of the day. That's the sort of bad publicity we could do without."

"I see. Hang on, it might be possible. I'll call you back."

About half an hour later, he phoned back with a plan: "Get yourself in the car and go round to a mate of mine. He's a second-hand car dealer, smashing feller. I've known him all my life and he'll see you all right. Don't, for God's sake, ask any questions. Just turn up at his used car lot as soon as you can and say who you are. He'll hand over a package with the exact amount in. I'll sort it all out with him and with you on Monday; you just go down and collect the money. But remember, no questions. Don't say too much, just take it and go."

Very cloak and dagger, I thought, as I put down the phone. What choice did I have? I couldn't risk this Scott character blackening Paul's name with his half-baked story. With some butterflies in my stomach I rang for the car and told the driver to take me to the address in south London that my mate had given me.

I don't think I could find that used car lot again, even if I had to. It was one of five hundred, all the same: rusty old Zephyrs and Crestas, piles of second-hand tires, and a corrugated iron hut used as an office. Yet the owner was as good as he'd been made out to be. I just went up to the hut, announced myself (just as Alistair, nothing to do with the Beatles) and took a brown envelope. In the back of the car, I counted it: £1118s in used banknotes and coins. Thank God for that.

"Now take me to Brixton prison," I told the long-suffering driver.

Trust my luck. You probably saw on television that there was a big escape from Brixton a few weeks ago. Some guy had arranged for his mates to drive a furniture van up to the wall. Then he'd climbed over the high wall and jumped down for a comfortable landing on top of the van, and so away. He couldn't do that now, because the prison authorities have put great big bollards across the end of the long road that leads past the wall to the main gate. All cars now have to park about half a mile away and anyone wanting to visit has to walk all the way down this depressing road past the wall. I didn't walk, I ran, getting more and more soaked with every second that passed, while the driver relaxed with a cigarette back in the car.

At last I was let into the prison, absolutely drenched because I'd forgotten to wear an overcoat.

Prison is just like they show it in the movies. Great hulking warders with hoop-la rings of keys on their hips, three lots of massive gates, parties of prisoners carrying round chamber pots with lids. All just the sort of thing any tourist wants to see at the weekend.

The chief warder was very pleasant, though, as we sat in his little office: "That's all right, Mr Taylor. Scott's in court at the moment, but the minute he comes back I'll have him brought straight here and we can sort out the official receipt and the paperwork for his release. If you'd like to wait in the waiting room along the corridor, I'll send for you when he's brought back."

That hour I spent in the waiting room just about completed my education, I reckon. It happened to be visiting time, and the room was full of prisoners" wives, most of them carrying great big cakes and bottles of orange juice or clutching bursting carrier bags full of other goodies. Some of the conversations were priceless.

"I didn't know your Charlie was inside again! What's he done now?"

"Oh, the silly sod! He only broke into the shop next door!"

They were talking about their husbands" crimes like you or I might talk about last night's television! And all the time there were miserable little parties of prisoners going past, carrying buckets and mops.

Finally, I saw the van come through the last set of gates and a file of prisoners in ordinary clothes were taken out of it. One of them had to be Scott. A few minutes later I was summoned to the chief warder's office, where I handed over the money and made sure I had an official receipt for it. I also made Scott sign a statement saying that he'd received a once-only payment with no liability and that he wouldn't be back asking for more. He didn't seem very grateful, but I didn't really care. All I wanted was to get out of that claustrophobic place, reeking of disinfectant and sweat, as soon as possible.

Scott and I were at last spat out of the intestines of the prison into the pouring rain. I was only too glad to be in the open again, rain or no rain. All Scott's mates were waiting outside to congratulate him.

As I started to walk back down the long road to where the car was parked, I heard Scott's voice shouting to me, "By the way, have you got a quid for a taxi?"

I kept on walking.

London

If you look at a map of Kent, you will see, lying a mile or so from the A2 road, a tiny village named Bean. It was here that "mute Beatlemania" was invented.

The telephone in my flat rang early one Saturday morning. As usual, I was wandering around in my dressing gown, hoping for a quiet day. Some hope! Paul was his usual chirpy self. Does he never want a day off with his feet up? He said, "Alistair, will you and Lesley come house-hunting with me?"

"Sure, Paul," I answered, as always.

"Pick you up in half-an-hour."

When Paul arrived, he was driving his Aston Martin DB6. The car was full already, with Paul's new girlfriend, Francie Schwartz, and Martha, his Old English Sheepdog, taking up the available space.

"We'll never all fit in there!" I protested. "That back seat's built for midgets!"

"Don't complain. Of course we'll fit in. You can share the back with Martha. You're good friends, aren't you?"

So off we went, Paul and Francie quite comfortable in the front, Lesley and me feeling as if we were sitting under a pile of rugs on a very narrow shelf. No one asked Martha how she felt! It was a very dreary day's pointless house-hunting; there was nothing that appealed to us at all.

On the way back to London, Paul suddenly stamped on the brakes and brought us to a smoking halt. When the blaring of horns from inconvenienced motorists behind us had died away, he turned to us and yelled, "Did you see that signpost? It said "Bean. One mile." I've got to go to Bean, just to say I've Bean there!"

At that, he made a sharp U-turn (more blaring of horns) and roared off down the road to Bean. Was this to be the place of Paul's dreams and fantasies?

Definitely not. Bean is not going to win any prizes for Britain's most attractive village and we found out very soon that the only magic was in the name. Rows and rows of identical houses confronted us, relieved only by the occasional shop-front and pub.

"This is a drag. Let's turn round in this pub car-park and go home."

As Paul said this, the pub doors opened. We were just in time for the first drinks of the evening, so we decided to have a swift one. We trooped, Martha as well, into a great barn of a pub, with a huge bar along one wall.

Paul casually said, "Evenin'," to the woman behind the bar and the others sat at a table while I bought a round. I could see the eyes of the middle-aged barmaid on Paul all the time. As she poured our drinks there was beer going down her arm and all over the floor because she wasn't looking at what she was doing. I could tell what she was thinking: "Can it be? No, not here, not in Bean? But it looks like him. I'm sure it's him..." The only thing she actually said was the price of our drinks and even when she took the money she didn't look at it, but kept her eyes fixed like radar-beams on Paul.

I went over to Paul with the drinks and said, "You've been rumbled again."

"Just look natural," Paul mumbled. "I want to be an ordinary guy. No crowds, no autographs, just a quiet drink."

It's very difficult to be natural when you're the only people in a big room, being devoured by someone's silent adoration. I didn't know where to look, but suddenly I was aware of more people behind the bar. I turned round and there, staring slack-mouthed and silent, were the landlady, her husband and two children! The worst about it was that they said nothing at all, not a whisper, not a murmur, not a peep.

There was a drum set on a platform at the other end of the bar, obviously put there by the night's group. Paul couldn't resist having a bash, so he walked over and amused himself for a few minutes. The family followed him with their eyes, their heads turning together like the turrets of a battleship, their ears doubtless noting for future reference every clash of the cymbals.

It was becoming a little wearing. Paul came down from the platform, we finished our drinks and walked out. As we left, Paul again said, "Evenin'." No reply. They just stared after us. It was all so eerily silent that I almost wondered if I'd been struck deaf. The Beatles make most people scream, but in Bean we struck them dumb!

15
CHAPTER

London

So now everyone knows that John and Yoko are in Gibraltar to get married. They've been hounded enough by the press, but they're now looking forward to a peaceful wedding on The Rock. A suitable place for such a besieged couple, I think.

Getting John and Yoko to Gibraltar was as tricky an operation as I can ever remember being involved in. They were in Paris, taking a short break, and they needed discreet transport. There were squads of pressmen, battalions of photographers and armies of TV cameras to avoid. All the world wanted to know where they were off to next. A suitable case for Mr Fixit to take on!

Mr Fixit decided that his role in all this was as air transport manager and money courier. The first task was simple: have an executive jet quietly parked at dawn on the tarmac of Le Bourget airport, well away from the main parking areas; make sure it was stocked with food, drinks, magazines and anything else which John and Yoko might need to sustain them on their flight and restore themselves after the usual car chase to the airport. The second task was also simple: have hanging inside my trousers a stocking filled with five hundred pounds in English currency for John and Yoko to spend in Gibraltar! That's a lot of money to carry around in cash, so I decided to keep it in that unorthodox place! Excuse me, sir, do you hang to the left or to the right?

So there I stood in today's chilly, misty dawn, sensing rather than seeing the watery rays of the sun coming over the horizon. Wherever I looked there was only the damp clinging fog; of the world's press there was no sign. For once, there hadn't been a leak from the organization. The steps of the jet were down, the door was open, the engines were warmed up. The crew and I waited only for the arrival of John and Yoko.

Suddenly, in the mist, appeared two more intense patches of white. For a second or two, I couldn't make out what or who it was, but then running towards the plane, laughing and holding hands, were John and Yoko. These weren't the serious-faced gurus of the imagination of the press; they were a young couple setting off on a tremendous adventure. Free from all worries and pressures, their laughter told anyone who was about in that chilly dawn that they were in love.

Up the steps into the jet they went, full of life and congratulations. We opened a celebration bottle of champagne and had a small party in the plane. We couldn't stop catching each other's eye and laughing. Eventually I wished them good luck and the door closed on them. Next stop Gibraltar. The pitch of the engines rose and the plane started to taxi slowly towards the runway.

Satisfied with the knowledge of a job completed, I walked over to the grass at the side of the runway, put my hands in my pockets...and froze! Still dangling down my inside leg was the stocking full of spending money! Oh no, John and Yoko would be paupers in paradise! How could I have forgotten to give it to them, after all, I had only two jobs to do and that was one of them!

Without thinking, I sprinted after the taxiing jet, somehow overtook it as it turned on to the take-off runway and I began to wave frantically at the pilot, mouthing, "Stop! Stop!" —as if he could hear anything above the hellish din of the engines. He stopped the plane just before I was sucked into those spinning jets, or so it felt. Down came the steps, and John's face appeared at the door. God knows what he was thinking as I started to struggle frantically with my trousers belt and zip! At last I pulled out the stocking and waved it at him, shouting a rough explanation. No, I'm not a secret transvestite!

The money was put aboard, the plane disappeared down the runway into the mist, and John and Yoko were soon together in the blue sky with their hopes and dreams.

Meanwhile, I made a leisurely readjustment of my clothing and awaited the late arrival of the press. Think of me when you buy your souvenirs, John and Yoko, and good luck to you both.

London

Well, today I realized a small ambition of mine and suffered the injury which has made my handwriting so shaky. It was a very tiny price to pay.

When the boys are down in the studio almost anything can happen. Anyone who's standing around is likely to be given an instrument and told "hit that" or "here, shake this'!

This afternoon some of us were downstairs in the studio listening to Paul doing some incredible jamming on his bass guitar. George came in, picked up his guitar and joined Paul, exchanging riff for riff like you never heard on a Beatles record. Ringo came down, took one look at Paul and George and sat down at his drum kit, matching the rhythm and underpinning the session. Anyone who thinks that only groups like Cream can jam like that is wrong, believe me!

The session must have been going on for half an hour, when Ringo shouted to me, "Come here." By the side of him was a pile of tambourines. He pointed to them and told me, "Play one of these."

"Yeah, why not?" I laughed, and I joined in, shaking with the best of them. Part of the time I was banging the tambourine against my hand, then when that got a bit sore I switched to my knee. The Salvation Army wasn't in it, as far as I was concerned!

The trouble with these jam sessions is that they don't give you any chance for a breather, so I was pretty relieved when my beeper went off after about a quarter of an hour and I had to go back to my office. Still, I've achieved an ambition that most professionals would give their eye teeth for —I've jammed with the Beatles! I hope the recorders weren't on!

The afternoon wore on with me working away on the mountain of paperwork that Apple generates every day. I reached out for a file and said to myself, "Ow, that hurts!" I looked down at the hand I'd been knocking the tambourine against and it was jet black with bruising! It wasn't too painful, but it looked as if somebody had been hitting it with a hammer.

Back home this evening Lesley wasn't too impressed when I told her how I'd come by my honorable wound. "You stupid idiot!" she laughed. Later on I discovered on my leg, stretching about six inches on either side of my knee, the big brother of the bruise on my hand! Two great black patches for just about fifteen minutes of tambourine thumping!

Now I'm lying in bed trying to write without knocking the bruises, which have come up quite painfully. At least I know two things that I never knew before about the girls in the Salvation Army: why they wear thick wool uniforms and why they keep varying the part of their bodies they knock the tambourines against! It's not for show, it's for survival!

London

After I bought the island, Dorinish, for John at that loopy auction, a kick-back came a few weeks later when I had a tax demand from the Irish government. I had to send that to Michael Browne (the son of Mr Browne, the auctioneer) who was still acting as solicitor for me. Of course, he didn't know who I was acting for, as all the deeds are in my name. I have deposited with John's solicitors a letter saying that he has all the rights to the island.

It was a long time before I took John out to the island. Then I rang Michael and told him the truth. He doesn't mind; he's getting the same money. Anyway, I took John and two friends out and we had a loony day there. It made a welcome change not to have to keep looking over our shoulders for press photographers or phalanxes of screaming fans. The nearest camera must have been five miles away.

We were walking along the causeway between the two parts of the island when John suddenly froze in his tracks and shouted, "Don't anybody move!" We looked down at where his gaze was fixed. Between the pebbles were hundreds of gulls" eggs, so we had to creep from pebble to pebble to avoid treading on them. It took hours to cross that causeway, but John wouldn't allow us to step on a single egg.

At last we reached the high point of the island, looking out over the Atlantic. John put his arm round my shoulder and said, "Alistair, that bit down there is yours to do what you like with. You can have that corner. Build on it. Do what you like." That was the last I've ever heard of that. Like an idiot, I never have got it in writing.

We flew out a second time with Magic Alex. He was talking about building a bubble-house that floated in mid-air above the island! Utterly crazy. It would have been blown half over Ireland in those winds. Alex is still figuring out designs for avant-garde houses.

The best thing, perhaps, is that the island is as unspoiled as it was on the day I bought it, and likely to remain so, with one exception. I thought that John had lost all enthusiasm for the place, but a few days ago he called me up and said, "I've got an idea; come on out to Kenwood." In the garden he has a beautiful genuine Romany caravan —the real thing. He took me out to it and said, "See that?"

"Yes, " I replied, "I've seen it hundreds of times. It's beautiful, but so what?"

"I want that on the island," he said. Imagine the prospect of transporting a Romany caravan from Weybridge to Clew Bay! But he was serious; it has to be done.

So off I flew back to Ireland and saw everyone again —we're good friends by now. We've had a great raft built by the local carpenter and we're going to put the caravan on to it and tow it out to Dorinish when the tide and weather are right —if ever they are.

The local people don't mind; it's good for trade. They've been making money out of foreigners since the Spanish Armada was wrecked on their shores. They all think it's a great joke, this pop star working out his fantasies on their little island (it'll always be "their" island).

I only hope John doesn't want a horse on the island as well —or, even worse, a full-time inhabitant. You know who'd be given the job!

London

That's the end of another week of recording at Abbey Road. I'm going straight home for a hot bath and twelve hours" sleep.

Most nights this week the boys have been recording till the small hours and after a while I began to feel that I don't quite have that youthful flush of energy any more. It'd be fine if I could sleep late in the morning, but I always like to be at the office early to open the mail —that old habit that Brian used to insist on.

Last night they'd been recording until about three o'clock and I could feel that I'd had enough. All I wanted to do was get my head down for three or four hours, but the boys just called a few minutes" break and went out of the room. The trouble was that I'm acting as a kind of personal assistant to Paul at the moment, on top of everything else, and I didn't feel that I could leave the studios without checking whether there was anything he needed. Where was he, though? I searched all over the place, which is a bit like the set from that old film *The Phantom of the Opera*, but he wasn't in any of the usual places.

At last I wandered into the huge Number One studio, the one where they record full symphonies. It's so big that you could just about fit a three-ring circus into it. certainly too big for us to use very often. Right of the far side was a little speck in the shadows —Paul sitting at the grand piano. The control room light was still on and I could see one of the technicians still at work on the tape machine behind the glass window.

As I walked over to Paul, I realized that he'd just finished recording a song and was winding down from it. With one hand, he was picking out a beautiful melody on the keys.

"I've just been recording a song for Marianne Faithfull."

"What, that one you've just been playing now?" I asked.

"No, no, this is just an idea I've got for a song," Paul replied off-handedly.

"But it's fabulous. The melody line is beautiful. Lesley would love that," I said wistfully.

"Hang on a minute," grinned Paul. He called over to the technician behind the window, "Have you got any tape left?"

"Yeah," the guy shouted.

"Right," murmured Paul, as he turned again to the keyboard. "You stand over there and shut up for a minute or two, Alistair."

I stood there just a few feet away while Paul composed a song out of this lovely melody, full of la-las and hums, but a song with shape and words, all for Lesley, and all in a few minutes of spare time. In three minutes, that song had grown from a casual one-fingered idea into another Beatles song. God, where do they all come from?

"Right, there you are," Paul yawned as he stood up and stretched. "I don't need you any more tonight. You can go home, and thanks for being here."

This morning Paul walked into my office and quietly put an acetate recording on to my desk. "Right. That's the only copy of the recording I made last night for Lesley. This is the tape we used and now there'll be no more copies made from it."

So saying, he unrolled the wide recording tape, took a pair of scissors from the desk and cut the tape into a dozen pieces, letting them fall into my wastepaper basket.

"That'll be the only copy in all the world."

"What do you call it, Paul? I asked.

""The Long and Winding Road"," he replied as he strolled off.

So now I have the only copy of that recording, possibly the only copy of Paul actually at work composing. I'd have stayed up ten nights on end to have that!

London

The boys played "Get Back" on the roof of the Apple offices in Savile Row and the concert was closed down by the police after complaints by the neighbors.

Well, I'm not surprised that it turned out like that. God knows, I'm no fuddy-duddy — ten years in show business have seen to that —but the Beatles can't expect to set up shop in Savile Row without upsetting a few of the neighbors. When I was helping to choose the new offices, we all knew well that we wouldn't be the most popular immigrants in what must be one of the most conventional streets in London. Now the concert has certainly wiped out any remaining chances of peaceful co-existence!

It's not so much the boys" attitude to the neighbors that bothers me —after all, they're not going to have a rooftop concert every day. No, what made me leave the office before the whole thing started was the trap they wanted to set for the police. The plan was to have a hidden camera set up in the entrance to the building so that, when the police arrived as we knew they would, they could be filmed as they closed down the concert.

There's nothing illegal in that, I'm sure, but it just seems ungrateful. People too often forget that Beatlemania could never have happened without the police to control the crowds and protect us all. Way back at that first reunion with the boys at the East Ham Granada I can remember the police holding back the sea of fans and the patrol car leading us safely through all the red traffic lights. Besides, whatever faults the police may have, and I've met a few bad ones in my time, my job at NEMS and at Apple has always been about achieving things by getting on well with people. Putting everyone's back up seems pointless.

So I just said, "Fine, you set up a secret camera. I can't stop you. But leave me out. I want no part of it."

When the time came for the concert to begin, I cleared my desk, slipped on my coat and listened to the music as part of the crowd that had gathered in Savile Row.

London

It's well over a year since Brian died and I miss his ability more and more as the days go by. Too many people have been saying that he wasn't the world's most astute businessman and that he ought to have made more money for the Beatles out of recording contracts and advertising. My reply is quite simple: he negotiated the best deals for recording that he could manage at the time and, as far as advertising and product endorsement are concerned, no one was really making the most of that sort of thing five years ago. I guess the Beatles could have been advertising toothpaste in 1965 if Brian had wanted them to, but he had standards which no amount of money could persuade him to drop and his artistes were always expected to maintain these standards to Brian's satisfaction. The same business code made him stick rigidly to the terms of all his contracts. As for Apple, he approved of it in principle, but he never wanted anything to do with the running of it. Perhaps he could see ahead to the state we're in now.

It's not that we're in the sort of financial trouble that would mean the bankruptcy court, more that we have no overall control and direction. Huge sums of money are spent on all sorts of luxuries and no one seems to have any kind of plan.

Somebody (no one's ever sure where these ideas start!) had the idea of equipping a dining room at Savile Row. Instead of taking visitors and guests out for expensive meals in restaurants, wouldn't it be a groove and also economical to have our own dining room and two cordon bleu chefs? That way we could entertain people magnificently and save on restaurant bills. So we made all the arrangements and opened our dining room. There's only one thing wrong with the scheme: people still go out for lunch and most of the time the chefs only have to cook for Peter Brown and Neil Aspinall! As for me, all I manage most of the time if I'm staying in the office is a toasted sandwich snatched between phone calls, but then I've never been that interested in food for its own sake.

Drink is another huge expense. We have a huge metal cabinet bulging with bottles of fine wines and spirits, more than you could drink in a year. Only half a dozen people at the office drink from it, yet the bills for drink at outside restaurants must be huge. The Press Office must hold the record for drinks orders; next to their consumption, the bottle or two of spirits that Neil and I each use in a week seems a mere gnatbite!

Furnishings are an unbelievable expense. One guy has an all-white office which cost the earth; I couldn't believe the bill when I saw it. Another has real antique furniture in his office and expensive old paintings all over the walls. I wouldn't mind if the boys had that sort of style, but we're meant to be the working executives!

I thought to myself, why shouldn't I have what I want, so I went out to Ryman's and bought a set of their office furniture which really took my eye. I didn't bother to ask the price, but when I found out that it happened to be the cheapest they make, I wasn't surprised. I don't care, as long as I like it. Anyway, Apple now provides Lesley and me with a marvellous flat in Montagu Place, near Marylebone, so I can't complain.

The recording studio in the basement has been an enormous drain on resources, too. The whole place has been converted at enormous cost, with no end of problems caused by a central heating boiler house sited just behind one of the thin walls. For a while, you could hear every gurgle and whoof that the boiler made! All this time Alexis is still promising to build his space-age thirty-two track recording desk. That hasn't appeared so far, but it wouldn't surprise me if he managed it. God knows what such a machine would cost, though.

Now, as General Manager, I suppose it's my responsibility to keep an eye on what goes on in the office. A few days ago I decided to grasp the nettle and tell the boys that I couldn't see how we could possibly go on like this for much longer. Telling them unpleasant facts isn't very easy. The only person who could ever really say no to them and make it stick was Brian. If anyone else were to tell them to calm down, they wouldn't take a shred of notice. Even a simple business meeting's hard enough to arrange. We actually went through a period when nobody was allowed to do any business until John's soothsayer had thrown the I Ching! In the corner of my office!

Anyway, I'm wandering off the point. I prepared myself carefully for what I was going to say and waited for the time when I could catch all the boys in the office at the same time. Then I put it to them as straight as I could. My set speech started off with a warning that they were going to lose all their money if they carried on like this. They could hardly expect this virtual multi-million pound business to be run by the people managing it at the moment: Neil Aspinall, who has some experience in accountancy and a very shrewd brain, but came into the Beatles as the road manager; Peter Brown, who is an excellent organizer of the Beatles, but came into the business as a kind of social secretary to Brian; and me, not a bad trouble-shooter, but basically a record shop salesman! Sure, we had accountants and solicitors, but the three of us weren't really the men to look after long-term planning and investment, I thought. I know my abilities and I also know my shortcomings!

What was really needed, I said, was a Beeching. (Doctor Richard Beeching was the guy who came in to sort out British Railways when they were in a mess a few years ago. When he took the job, he found all sorts of waste and inefficiency and to cure this he started a great plan of closures and cutbacks designed to make the railways less unprofitable, even if they didn't make money.) What we needed was someone like him, an experienced top-quality businessman, to come in and take control of the long-term planning of Apple.

Would you believe it? Yesterday I found out that John and Yoko have gone to see Beeching and asked him to come and sort out Apple! I didn't mean it quite as literally as that! Apparently, he was very civil to them and chatted for a while, but his answer was always going to be no. The man's just in a different league.

Still, I suppose that visit shows that they've taken my comments to heart and whoever they eventually choose to run Apple will come as a relief to me!

16
CHAPTER

London

About a week ago, I was beavering away in my office at Apple when Paul rang. Could I come over to Cavendish Avenue right away, please? Four o'clock in the afternoon isn't the best time to cross London, but I dutifully called for my car and sat in the queues until I reached Paul's house. At least no one can hassle me in a car and I can let the driver do all the work. Not learning to drive was the best thing I never did, if you see what I mean!

Cavendish Avenue has seen a few changes recently. Everything's a bit different now that Paul's with Linda Eastman; I guess he doesn't need his old friends quite as much!

As I was driven over, I wondered whether there was any hitch in the travel arrangements I'd made for Paul and Linda's mini-holiday. I couldn't think of any, but you never know in the Beatles business. If there was any problem, I wouldn't have much time to sort it out —they were due to leave at seven o'clock.

Paul invited me in and said, "Right, Alistair. I'd like the whole of the ground floor of the house decorated by the time we come back."

"Are you serious, Paul? Do you know how long it takes to find anybody to do a decent decorating job in London these days?

Paul was absolutely serious. I was left in no doubt at all in the next half-hour, as he took me on a lightning conducted tour of the ground floor, occasionally referring to a paint color chart. Everything had been planned down to the last lick of paint and the last carpet nail. The carpet in the huge drawing room was pulled up to reveal beautiful woodwork ('I want that polished and restored, but not to look like your ordinary G-Plan."); the Indian-restaurant flock wallpaper in the dining room was to go; the kitchen was to be stripped and the original wood exposed and varnished; paintwork to be renewed and so on and so on, until my head was reeling with details.

Paul saved the worst bit until the end: "Now then, mate, when we get back, I want it to be all done, and I don't want to see so much as a paint brush in the house!"

A mere five days! Impossible, even for Mr Fixit, surely. I argued with Paul as much as I dared. Something was driving him on to this redecoration, I could see, because he was absolutely flat certain that it must be done.

"You can do it, Al. Never mind the cost. Just get it done."

They say Rome wasn't built in a day, but now I know why it took a thousand years. Five days to find and organize a reliable and trustworthy firm of decorators, shift all the furniture, pull up and chuck out yards and yards of carpet, strip and polish floors, paint acres of woodwork and have it all spanking clean and new! At least Paul hadn't ordered me to tell the paint makers to come up with an odorless paint!

Here's where Mr Fixit again made use of his spider's web of contacts and friends of friends, but even a spider's web can break if you pull at it too hard. I was driven back to Savile Row with my mind reeling with all the possibilities (and impossibilities). He's out of the country, they're tied up in Liverpool, oh God, who's left? That's it. My old friend John Lyndon, he'll know.

John did know. "Try Taverner's. They're the best."

Back to the telephone directory, hands trembling, not a moment to lose. Ah, a bonus. Taverner's are based in St John's Wood, just down the road.

Ian Taverner listened to my request in silence, until I came to the five days" limit. I had to take the receiver away from my ear as he doubled up with helpless laughter at the other end of the line.

"It's out of the question. Absolutely impossible in the time you want. Five weeks would be a better bet."

"I haven't got five weeks," I replied desperately. "Can you at least meet me at Cavendish Avenue tomorrow and see what you can do...please?"

"All right, but I can't promise anything at all. We'd better meet early, just in case. Would eight tomorrow morning suite you?'

Would it! I didn't get much sleep that night, wondering how it could be done and what Paul would say if it wasn't. I think even Brian would have admitted the impossible on this one.

I was at Cavendish Avenue at half past seven, smoking furiously and looking at my watch every two minutes. I needn't have worried about Ian, though; he was absolutely punctual. Brian would have liked that. I let us in and he took a really professional look at the ground floor, with me following and itching to ask him if he could do it.

When we'd covered all the ground and he'd asked me about two hundred questions, Ian stood with a thoughtful look on his face. I didn't like to break the silence, but at last he said, "What a great challenge! I'd love to have a crack at it."

Back in the car we carried on sorting out the details. I had to be absolutely sure that Ian could do it — remember, not a paint brush to be left in the house!

"Yes, I think we can do it, Mr Taylor."

"Ian, there's no question of *think* you can. If you take it on, you have to be sure you can do it. There's a lot riding on this."

In the end, Ian asked for two hours to draw up some time sheets and look at the workload and, sure enough, true to his word, he telephoned me at the office. His men would have to work through the nights, changing shifts every eight hours, but it could be done. He actually guaranteed that it would be done with six hours to spare —and not a paint brush left in the house!

"OK, Ian. Go for it."

If anyone ever tells you that the British workman doesn't work, send them round to Taverner's. I must say that I wasn't absolutely sure about how reliable they'd be until I'd spent a day dropping in on them to check. They are a superb firm. They haven't just decorated the rooms, they've restored them. Every hairline crack in the plaster and woodwork was made good with filler, every trace of the old wallpaper was stripped off using a wonderful steam machine, every surface was rubbed down and carefully prepared before it even saw a paint brush. On the fourth day, they even asked my permission to carry on up the stairs to the first floor, just to round off the job, while Paul's wooden floor shone like marble. Utterly superb workmanship.

I went up to the house every few hours, but it was pretty clear that there was no need to. After the first day I went just to admire the skill and the speed they worked with. I love to see people doing a job they're good at, and adding a bit of dash and style to it.

On the appointed hour, six hours before Paul and Linda were due back, I went up to the house and found the foreman backing out of the front door, checking to see that there was nothing to show that they'd been there! He need not have bothered, and I need not have checked either. Not a paint brush in sight, and very little smell.

As the time for Paul and Linda's return drew closer, I lit the fire and put on the kettle, grinning to myself at the thought of what they were about to find. Paul's face said it all. He admitted that he hadn't thought I could do it, but he was just dumbfounded at what had been done. I asked him to look for the dreaded paint brush, and we all had a laugh over it.

So everyone's happy. Paul and Linda have a newly-decorated ground floor and Paul certainly looks better for his holiday. I think he was fairly bushed when he left, or he'd never have been so pushy about it. Taverner's reputation is even more golden, deservedly so. Lastly, Mr Fixit has kept his unbeaten record —and that's worth a sleepless night or two!

All I have to do now is take the bill up to Paul when it arrives. It won't be cheap, but it won't be a rip-off either; Ian Taverner knows a fair deal when he sees one.

London

Well, that bill from Ian Taverner arrived yesterday morning. It was a lot less than I'd expected. I never had thought that the job could have been done so well so quickly and, besides, Paul did tell me that I wasn't to worry about the cost. Off I went to Cavendish Avenue, in quite a good mood, still pretty smug about it all.

Paul and Linda sat on the big settee in front of the fire while I produced the bill with a big grin on my face. Paul looked at it for a few seconds and said, "Great! Get the check to them, Alistair."

I relaxed even more and was just about to put the bill back in my briefcase when Linda reached for it. I gave it to her —what the hell, she's Paul's girlfriend and she had as much right to see it as he did. She looked at it for a long minute, then accused Ian Taverner of overcharging Paul. Not only that, but she asked me how much I'd made out of the deal! I could not trust myself to speak; my spine and limbs were cold with rage and my mouth was too dry to utter a word. I just stood up, closed my briefcase and walked out of the room.

Paul came after me and tried to act as peacemaker, but I didn't want to know. In the office this morning, be brought up the subject again and I just wouldn't talk about it. OK, Linda's got a right to be concerned on Paul's behalf, fair enough. I know that Lesley would do the same. But if Linda knew me better I can't believe she'd make the sort of suggestion she did.

London

Sometimes, here in the Apple offices, it seems as if it's the rest of the world that's the dream and we're the crazy reality. I don't know how long it can last and I don't know how long I can last. There's a definite feeling that the trip's turned bad.

Our relationships here aren't what they were, either. If only we could put back the clock to the old innocent days at the East Ham Granada or the Finsbury Park Astoria or even the Tower Ballroom, if only we could put the boys back on stage and let them blast away the cobwebs of uncertainty and illusion which have trapped us all. But we can't, and if we could we'd only ride the same old crazy switchback to this office and this decaying Apple Corps. Brian, where are you now?

There's been another incident between me and Linda, I'm afraid. Paul's got this fabulous Aston Martin DB6, a real James Bond machine but without the rockets. It's a car I've enjoyed many journeys in, but a few weeks ago it wasn't looking in the best of health. Paul had just had it serviced and he was in the office complaining about the standard of the work the garage had done.

"You know, when they do what they call a full service, nobody ever thinks to clean out the ashtrays!"

I knew what he meant. That's a typical McCartney way of asking why didn't the garage restore the car to its proper pristine showroom condition, clean ashtrays and all.

"OK," says I, "next time let me organize it and I'll bring it back to you with more than the ashtrays cleaned." Big mouth.

Not so long ago, Paul took me up on the offer. He walked into my office with the usual McCartney boyish grin on his face and reminded me of my scheme.

"Not only that, Alistair, but I want it re-sprayed. Get some color cards and I'll pick a shade. You get it done, fully serviced and re-sprayed, and I want it to come back as if it has just been driven out of the showroom."

Now there was an added problem, as if I don't already have enough to do trying to keep my finger in the crumbling dyke-wall of Apple. Still, I had volunteered and I couldn't really say no (as usual).

But came the great day when the work was complete. I had the guy who'd done the job drive the Aston with great care to Cavendish Avenue, where we all inspected it. It was an utterly marvellous job, paintwork (which was the original British Racing Green — fourteen coats) looking better than new, inside totally restored, even the tires black-painted and polished — and of course, clean ashtrays! Paul walked around it, lost in amazement, and eventually eased himself into the driving seat, absolutely thrilled. It was like the meeting of two old friends. Paul couldn't stop saying how good the work was and how pleased he was.

Linda saw the bill (reasonable enough) and made exactly the same sort of accusations as she made over the decorating of Cavendish Avenue. As far as I'm concerned, Paul can now ask somebody else to look after his domestic work. I've had enough.

Over the Channel

Here I am flying over the English Channel on a beautiful spring morning on my way for a holiday in Ibiza. I've been sacked from Apple. It hurts even to write it down, but there's no escaping it. My connection with the Beatles has been cut, and by a man whom I've never even met.

On Thursday I had an appointment with a guy who'd come over from Hawaii to try to book some of our acts. I knew what that meant — the Beatles. He'd be lucky. Anyway, he came to the office and we were talking about the prices for Gerry and the Pacemakers and Billy J. Kramer and Cilla, but he wanted to offer us a million dollars to stage a Beatles reunion concert. This happens quite often and the answer is always the same; the Beatles no longer play together in public. Their last tour performance was at Candlestick Park in San Francisco as long ago as August 1966. That's it, apart from the "Get Back" rooftop session at Savile Row.

In the conversation it came out that this guy was also in Europe for a meeting of FIFA, the governing body of international soccer. Ah-ha, thought I. It's the Cup Final very soon and the boys often ask me (usually on the very morning) to arrange some tickets for them, especially if Liverpool or Everton are playing. Now this usually strains even my talents for fixing to the limit; now that I had a tame football official in my clutches I wasn't going to let him go without trying to extract some Cup Final tickets from him!

"Can you get some Cup Final tickets for us, please?" I asked.

"Oh, I have a quota," he replied innocently.

"Ah, why don't we have some lunch?" I suggested, homing in on my prey.

Off we went to my favorite restaurant, the Capri, just about a quarter of a mile from the office, telling my secretary where we were going and that I'd be back about three o'clock. The lunch was very pleasant, and I'd managed to persuade my guest to part with four Cup Final tickets, when I was called to the telephone by Gerry, the proprietor.

What a drag, I thought. We've only just finished the main course. It can't be important.

Peter Brown was on the line, "Can you come over to the office, please?"

"I can't at the moment, Peter," I replied. "I've got a guest here and we're having lunch."

"I know that," he insisted. "But can you come back now?"

"Peter, unless it's a crisis, the answer is no."

"It is a crisis, Alistair."

What the hell could this be? Peter could run everything perfectly well. What could he possibly want me for? Still, a crisis is a crisis and I had better go. I went over to my guest and apologized for my hasty departure, promising to be back as quickly as possible. Meanwhile, Gerry would serve him with whatever he wanted and it would be put on my account.

As I walked into Peter's office, he was sitting in his swivel chair sideways on to me. I sat down and waited for him to finish his telephone conversation with Ron Kass. In his hand was a piece of paper with what appeared to be a list of names.

"Yes, Ron, I'm afraid they're both sacked," said Peter into the telephone.

I knew at once why I'd been called back. Peter put down the phone and spun round in his chair.

"Me as well?" I asked.

"Yes," he answered.

He handed me the list, which had on it over a dozen names, all numbered, with my name at the head of the list — Number One.

"When?" I asked.

"Today."

"You are joking, aren't you?" I gasped.

"No, I'm not," Peter replied sadly. "Alistair, I wanted to tell you myself before one of Allan Klein's people told you."

I gathered what strength I had in my shaking limbs.

"Fair enough, Peter, but I'll tell you one thing. If I go today watch out for the bonfire where I'll be burning all the private papers and documents I keep for the boys in the safe box in my flat. I'm not coming back here with them!"

"Oh, you wouldn't do that, would you?" he asked. "Anyway, the boys have said that they want me to take especial care of you."

"What does that mean?" I asked, feeling like a racehorse put out to grass instead of being shot.

"Three months" salary and you keep the flat for three months, while you find something else."

"I'm not leaving today, anyway. You know I'm going away by myself on Sunday for this holiday in Ibiza. I'll need to come in and clear up all the outstanding work. I'll go when I'm ready."

Peter must have known that the only reason that I'm going on this holiday is because I've contracted glandular fever partly through overwork and I'm under doctor's orders to go.

What the hell was I to do? I left the office with Peter's words pounding in my head, all thoughts of my guest marooned in the restaurant forgotten. Allan Klein, now that he's gained control of Apple, seems to want to rid the organization of as many people as he can who were there in the old days. To think it was me who first put the idea into the boys" heads that they needed a Beeching, a man who'd cut out the dead wood and make the place efficient. Never has a man more truly signed his own death warrant!

All the way down the stairs I was passing other unfortunates who'd just received their bad news. Some of them were already moving out their personal effects, others were wandering around in a daze, with their severance money in their top pockets. It was as brutal as that.

The boys stayed right out of it. I went back to my office and picked up the phone, not to plead for my job back, but just to make sure they knew what was being done. Could they really be permitting this to happen to me after all these years, all the shared times?

Not one of them would speak to me, although I could hear voices in the background which I thought belonged to some of them. They were not in to my call. It hurt me more than I can say that they could not bring themselves to speak to me and let me be sacked by a man I'd never met.

Like a dead man continuing to walk through sheer automatic power, I went on through that dreadful day, still working for the Beatles, clearing my desk and wondering how I'd tell Lesley the news. We were having guests for dinner that evening, a charming American couple whom we'd met in the Capri Restaurant, of all places.

I didn't tell Lesley that night, preferring to drink too much at dinner and put on a clown act to cover my confusion. How I made my way through the meal I do not know. All Friday I worked at the office, clearing up, determined not to leave anything undone, and on Friday evening I went home and told Lesley.

She was in the bedroom as I walked in and dumped my briefcase down on the bed. She was in the big walk-in wardrobe, totally invisible behind the racks of clothes.

"Come here, love. I've got something to tell you."

Her voice came from inside the wardrobe. "I know. You've been fired."

"Yeah."

She put her head round the door. "Oh, in that case we'll show them, won't we?"

That was when I burst into tears and she came to comfort me, sitting on the arm of the chair with her arm around me.

"Let it go, love. Don't bottle it up."

We decided that I'd still go on this trip. Lesley was never going to come; foreign travel is not her scene at all. She absolutely insisted that I carry on with the holiday, since it's a matter of my health. But I couldn't bring myself to use the hire car we'd booked to take me to Gatwick airport. It seemed too much of an expense for an unemployed man. Lesley had other ideas.

"No way," she said. "No way. You are going to carry on as before until you get back. Then we'll see about economizing."

Sometimes it's better not to argue!

I rang up Don Murfitt, who has been supplying the boys with chauffeur-driven cars for years, and asked him for a car to take me to Gatwick. Nothing special, whatever he happened to have spare in his garage. Don, of course, has no idea I've been sacked; it was a simple business arrangement for him. Sure, he'd have a car waiting for me at half-past twelve this Sunday morning.

Earlier today Lesley and I had a drink with some friends who wanted to see me off. We came out of the pub at about twenty past twelve and walked back to the flat. Just outside was parked a white Rolls-Royce. Now, John has a white Rolls-Royce and I assumed it must be his.

"Oh no, that's John's Rolls. That's all I need."

As we drew nearer I realized that it wasn't big enough to be John's car. Strange.

Standing on the steps leading to our flat was an immaculate chauffeur in full livery.

"Mr Taylor?"

"Yes?'

"This is your car, sir."

"There must be some mistake. I didn't order a Rolls."

"No, sir. This is your car. Mr Murfitt's orders."

In I climbed with Lesley, who was coming to the airport to see me off. We absolutely got the giggles as we pulled into Gatwick because we could see people craning to see who was in the big white Roller! It must be a film star and his lady behind those dark glasses.

"Will you wait while we have some lunch?" I asked the chauffeur.

"Of course, sir." And he not only waited, but he parked the Rolls right outside the main doors in the No Waiting zone.

"You can't park here," I protested. "Where will you be when we've finished?"

"I shall be here, sir," he insisted, with deferential politeness. He was true to his word. He stood next to the car in the No Waiting zone until we'd eaten lunch; then he ran Lesley back home.

I can't believe that Don hasn't somehow found out about my sacking and has decided to give me one last treat. Certainly it was a stylish way to end my years with the Beatles. I only wish certain people in the Apple organization had been there to see it!

So what happens now and where I go now is all in the balance. Oh, I know I've been fired before and I've found myself back in the office the next day, but this is different. This time, I haven't been fired so much as axed.

London

I'm not too broken up by all that's happened at Apple. I had a marvellous holiday in Ibiza and I've come back ready to face whatever the next chapter brings. It may not be as exciting as working with the boys, but it might mean that I spend more time at home. And if I never enjoy the high life again, then I can at least say that I lived a bit once: saw Beatlemania from inside, travelled everywhere first class, used the best hotels, saw the insides of palaces, was there at events which people will still be talking about in fifty years, perhaps even helped change the world a little. No regrets.

When I arrived back at Gatwick, I wondered what Don Murfitt might have sent to pick me up. It wasn't a Rolls-Royce this time, just a rather splendid Jaguar, and Don himself was driving. Of course, the news had long since broken that I had been fired, but I still wanted to know why I'd been taken to Gatwick so luxuriously.

"You must have known about my being fired. How come you knew so soon?" I asked Don.

"I didn't know."

"Come off it, Don. You've never sent me a Rolls. You know me, I wouldn't mind if you sent me a Mini."

"I honestly didn't know. That was the only car available in the garage. As far as I'm concerned you get the best. I wouldn't let you down even if it meant sending the finest car I've got. I know Apple isn't paying for this trip, so you can have it free, on me. Think of it as a thank you for all you've done for us over the years."

It's good to know that people still care and more than ironic that I slipped into unemployment in the back of a white Rolls-Royce!

17
CHAPTER

Over the Atlantic

I'm back with the Beatles again, in a way, and returning from one of the most exciting weeks I can remember in the last decade and a half!

After I was switched off from Apple I didn't want to talk about it to anyone. I was asked to write my story quite soon afterwards, but the condition was that I had to provide "dirt'. No way, I said. There was so much trust invested in me by everyone at NEMS Enterprises and Apple over the years that I couldn't break it just to provide another sensational exposure of my friends. So there it rested.

After some adventures, I drifted out of show business and eventually came to work at the hotel in Matlock. There I'd be, serving drinks behind the bar, and every so often the conversation would turn to the Beatles and how they'd changed popular music and how the world has never been the same since. You know the kind of things people say. If only they knew who they're talking to, I'd think, but I generally kept quiet.

One day, I dug out that beautiful photograph I took of John sitting on a chair at Alex's father's house in Athens. Why not have some posters printed of it, I thought, and try to sell them in the Beatles shop in Liverpool? So off I went back over the hills to Liverpool, optimistic as usual, with a roll of posters under my arm. I must still have a little of the old luck left, because I arrived at the shop on the day of the official opening to the press. A lot of old faces were there and I was greeted like a long-lost relation. Where had I been? What was I doing now? Even the local press wanted to do an interview with me. But the biggest surprise came when my old friend Ian Wallace came over to me.

"Alistair, there's someone who'd very much like to meet you," he said, and introduced me to a denim-clad American.

His response to my name was total amazement: "Not the Alistair Taylor!"

Fame at last! It turned out that this guy's a lecturer in Beatle Studies at an American University — yes, you can actually do a course about the Beatles! Only then did I truly realize how much the legend was living on.

Now that I'd been pulled out of the woodwork, the Beatles machine wasn't going to let go of me that easily. Would I go to a Beatles Fan Club convention in Liverpool the following Sunday? I wasn't so keen and said I'd think about it, but when I arrived home Lesley insisted that I should go, however embarrassed I might be.

The convention was held in the Adelphi Hotel, with a gathering of nearly two thousand people. Again, I was amazed to see the interest that the boys still generate, even fifteen years on. Of course, my arm was slightly twisted again! Would I come on stage and answer a few questions for ten minutes? The fans would love to hear some of my tales. Up I went in front of this audience and Bob Wooller asked me questions for a little while.

It seemed to go well enough, I thought, as I turned to leave the stage. Hello, what's this? There's a great crowd of people blocking my way, waving autograph books and looking expectant. Is there someone famous behind me? I actually turned round to look and then I realized that they wanted my autograph! I couldn't believe it, but that night my aching hand persuaded me that it hadn't been a dream. I sat at a table and signed autographs for an hour and a half while the queue snaked into the distance.

Now that my name was back in circulation and people knew my address, it wasn't very long before the American Beatles fans wanted to hear more. This July I had a phone call from a guy called Mark Lapidus. He lives in New Jersey and he and his wife run a series of Beatles conventions in the States called Beatlefests. What I'd seen in Liverpool only half-prepared me for the invitation which followed. Mark wanted me to come to New York as a special guest speaker at this September's Beatlefest! Yes, please!

On the British Airways jet to New York I wondered what I was going to say to the American fans. I rummaged around in my bay and found the notepad on which I'd scribbled a few reminders: "John and Yoko at Le Bourget', "Bean', "Ringo's Pool Table'. In the end, I didn't write another thing. I was far too excited at being airborne again after fifteen years. I was sure that I'd think of something when it was my turn to talk.

New York seemed even bigger and noisier than it had on my last visit in 1967, but Mark rang me at the airport to welcome me and sent a car to take me to the Penta Hotel, where the Beatlefest was to be held. I was due to stay in the hotel for a week, and the Beatlefest was to take place on the Saturday and the Sunday in the middle of my stay.

The Penta is a massive place with a ballroom capable of holding three or four thousand people. On the Saturday, I went up to the ballroom to check on the positioning of my chair and the microphones. There were a few people beginning to take their places, but I took no notice of them and went off again. About half an hour before the start I went up to the ballroom again, just to see how things were going. There were about three thousand people sitting there waiting for me to talk to them!

I went cold and for the first time I began to wonder what I was doing there. I must be mad, I thought, to have come all this way and to have allowed myself to be billed so importantly, when I hadn't even made any notes. There was not only the question of whether I could give the talk. Should I give it? After keeping my silence for all these years, was it right to step into the spotlight?

With all this whirling about in my head, I went down to the bar, intent on breaking a golden rule and having a drink to settle my nerves. I bought a drink and went to sit down at one of the tables, trying to stop my teeth from chattering. Now I hadn't really noticed the piped music in the bar; it was nothing special — until the most amazing thing happened.

Suddenly the track that was playing stopped, even before it had finished, and a new record came on. It was the first song that Brian ever tipped for success in my presence, the song that I'd never thought would make it but which became a world-wide hit, the song which Brian reminded me about just a month before his death. "So you think that record's not going to be a hit, Alistair? Well, don't you remember "Georgia on my Mind"?"

As Ray Charles" voice came over the loudspeaker singing the unforgettable lyrics which I hadn't heard for so many years, it was almost as if Brian were there beside me, saying, "It's all right, Alistair. Go and tell them about the good times. I don't mind. You'll do fine." I looked around as the music faded, quite expecting to see Brian standing there, but of course there was no one.

I was left with the deepest feeling of confidence and comfort. All I wanted to do was go up the stairs to the ballroom and speak to the fans. And that's just what I did, without notes, just rolling from story to story. I was due to speak for an hour, but it was more like an hour and a half later that I took my standing ovation from the wonderfully warm audience.

Then the phone didn't stop ringing in my hotel suite. There was another talk on the Sunday and two question and answer discussion panels, interviews with the press and radio stations and a slot on the *Good Morning, New York* breakfast television program. On the last night of my stay, Mark and Carol Lapidus took me to the Windows on the World restaurant right at the top of one of the twin towers of the World Trade Center. As we ate, we could see the whole of Manhattan spread before us like a Monopoly board. As the sun went down, all of New York put on its lights, with the Empire State Building standing out proudly, unforgettable.

So here I am on the flight back, with an invitation to talk to the Los Angeles Beatlefest in November. I'm lost for words to describe the effect the Beatles still have on people. All I can think of is Brian and me sitting in the Cavern that lunchtime, thinking, "They're something special. Let's manage them." And they were. And we did.

18
CHAPTER

Three Years On...

After all this time I've almost forgotten what it's like to relate a real Beatles story! I have made numerous wonderful trips to America for BEATLEFEST, and all my other Beatle flavored trips, but this time I have, perhaps, the most marvellous story of all!

I've had a reunion with Paul!! Yes, after 21 years, we've come face to face, and given each other a big hug!

Paul gave his "Let It Be Liverpool" Concert on the banks of the Mersey, last June, 1990. Well, I wasn't going to go, but the day before the concert, my Merseybeatle friend, Bill Heckle, rang me up, about something else, and then said "Are you coming up tomorrow night?" When I said no, he said "Oh, only I might be able to fix it for you to meet up with Paul, just might!"

I ended up speaking to Geoff Baker, Paul's personal Press Officer for the tour, a lovely man. He gave me exact directions as to where to contact him at Kings Dock, and that was it! Needless to say, I couldn't wait.

Then the saga began. There was no time to get a proper pass organized of course. "Just go to the Press entrance and ask for me." I set off for Liverpool in my trusty if rusty car, "Boris", and arrived safe and sound, parked, and got myself to the Press entrance, in good time, about 5:30pm. Then I came up against "the wall". No pass, no entry!!

I must say, the young chap was very pleasant, but I must wait for the lady in charge to return, as she wasn't on intercom. So Alistair waited, and waited, and waited, along with several others in a similar position!!

Finally, she returned. I explained that I'd been told personally by Geoff Baker, to ask for him, and he would confirm to her that I was to be admitted. Off she went again, returning in about 15 minutes, gave out VIP badges to all — except me!! She handed me two standing room tickets for the show. "Do I get to the Press tent with these?" "Oh, no, but you can be in at the concert"

I kept very calm, handed them back quietly informing her that I had not come over the mountains just to attend the concert, with the prospect of driving back in the early hours of the morning. Something must have shown, either in my voice or my expression, 'cause she started to ask me my connection, so I explained what I'd been to Paul and the boys all those years ago. She said, "Please give me five minutes. Please do wait!"

She went off again, returning at almost a run, very embarrassed, thrust a gold VIP badge at me and said, "Please follow me." Off we set, together with two other fellows, and as we went behind the huge stage, there ahead was the Press and VIP tent. As we arrived, she shepherded the other two toward it, holding me back, and then directing to another, unmarked tent. "You go there Mr. Taylor."

Not knowing what the devil what was going on, I did as I was told!! It transpired that there were red badges, VIP and Press, and the Gold ones — family, really close friends — so there I was!!

There was Linda, looking great, and we waved across the crowd!! Paul was nowhere to be seen, so after a long chat with George Martin, someone else I've not seen for all these years, I overheard someone tell Linda she was wanted in the Press tent. I followed, and there was Paul, surrounded by a crowd of local dignitaries, chatting away about his schooldays. I stopped at the back, slightly to one side. I just didn't want to be too obvious.

As he was talking he glanced around, saw me, stopped in mid sentence, a big grin crossed his face, and of course, all heads turned to look at this faceless guy!! I stepped forward and went to shake hands — Paul just grabbed my hand, pulled me forward, and we just hugged each other — it was a fantastic feeling to meet up with him again after so long. Sadly, we only had a few minutes, as he was off to get set for the show — If only security hadn't been so tight, we could have had longer.

He insisted on having my card, so now I look forward to hearing form him sometime. When he has time, I'm sure I will. A friend took a couple of pics of our reunion, one for the family album.

Needless to say, the concert was sensational. Paul really pulled out all the stops for Liverpool, and to be in there with over 25,000 scousers, on the banks of the Mersey singing "Give Peace A Chance" and "Hey Jude" leaves a memory that will always be with me.

What an evening!!